1

THE HIDDEN SCIENCE OF
MELANIN

BY

LEON MARSHALL

Published in 2022 by Hidden Science Publishing
© The Hidden Science Academy 2022

ISBN - 978-1-7396980-0-3

Author: Leon Marshall
Illustration: Jeremy Salmon
Design and layout: WeDesign Media

PREFACE

When? When shall we start being honest? When are we going to start having honest conversations about melanin? Too often when melanin is brought up in a public forum it is met with disingenuous debates and discord. Those who talk about melanin in a positive light are accused of being divisive by pointing out the obvious differences in skin complexion and melanin pigments produced by humans. How does knowing the different types of melanin that exist in human beings cause division? There are different types of pigments that exist in plants. Does knowing this cause division between plant lovers? Why is the talk of melanin met with such opposition, such disdain; especially amongst those who seem to be fascinated by it the most? Why isn't melanin taught in schools? Does the educational system truly believe that it's unimportant? If it's unimportant why is melanin at the forefront of bioelectronic developments? What is bioelectronics?

When are we going to start having honest conversations about the biology of skin? Or the chemistry of humors? I'm not trying to be funny here, but "humors" in ancient physiology meant the four fluids of the body that were thought to determine a person's temperament, complexion, character and make-up. The colour or "hue" of a person's humors indicated the physical, mental and emotional wellbeing of that human. I find it quite humorous that this is never discussed. When are we going to start having honest conversations about "hue" or colour? For those of you who "don't see colour" why does this statement only apply to certain situations? You seem to see colour when you're at a traffic light. You seem to see colour when you're looking at fruits and vegetables. Why is your colour blindness selective? If you did see colour, perhaps in another human being, what would happen to that human being? Would they end up dead hanging from a tree? If not, maybe it's ok to see colour?

Is it too much to ask for people to be honest? Honest about what? Well, history for a start. Are we ever going to be honest about the lynching's during slavery where black men used to be castrated and skinned? Their melanated skin was then used to make clothing, belts, shoes, furniture and other souvenirs for white families to keep. Sofas and chairs, some of which are still around today, were stuffed with the afro hair of slaves to give the chair's more cushion. Shall we sweep this history under a rug and act like it never happened? Shall we pretend that their skin was never eaten as part of cannibalistic rituals or for medicinal purposes? Speaking of medicine, when are we going to start having honest conversations about what started modern medicine as we know it today? When are we going to tell people that it all started with the dried, often powdered flesh of embalmed Egyptian corpses? Why were black mummified corpses considered medicine? Anthropology has proven that all excavated mummies had considerable quantities of melanin in their skin. Shall we start being honest about the ethnicity of the Ancient Egyptians or shall we just continue to make movies where the Ancient Egyptians are played by white European actors?

What stops us from coming together and having open and honest science-based discussions about melanin? Dishonesty! In a world where being dishonest about science is becoming the new norm, honest discussions seem to be as out-dated as 4G. If we're being honest, human beings are more similar than they are different. However, anytime the differences are mentioned for some strange reason detesters come crawling out of the woodwork with claims of racial division and "pro-black" rhetoric. The detesters never seem to have a problem with the medical industry pointing out these differences. The medical industry is constantly making us aware that black blood donors are needed for sickle cell patients or that black people are more prone to the common diseases of society. According to the medical industry Black women in the UK and the US are more likely to die from complications surrounding pregnancy and childbirth; and Black men are more likely to die from prostate cancer. We are never told why though; have you noticed this pattern? So those who are told that they are more at risk are left scratching their head wondering "why me?" If these claims from the medical industry are true then there are distinct biological differences between human beings that should be explored. Exploring these differences will not divide truth seekers; for there's nothing divisive about the truth. Genuine truth seekers gravitate towards it like a magnet. What better way to come together and be united than through truth. We should all be able to speak the truth about melanin without insecure individuals complaining that it promotes black supremacy (what on earth is that?!), black genetic dominance or some other erroneous thought they may have in their mind about melanin-based knowledge. These are all disingenuous, dishonest counter-arguments to cause confusion around a topic that we all want to know about.

All we want to know is the truth. Hence, the aim of this book is to spark honest conversations about the true science of melanin, which is hidden in plain sight. With that being said I'd like to make a disclaimer about the content of this book. This book is a scientific conversation starter. Use this book to start conversations with friends and loved ones that you might not have been able to start previously due to a lack of accurate information. The information contained in this book is based on science and not opinion. It is intended to inform and educate the reader about melanin and how melanin behaves inside living organisms. Everything stated about melanin in this book is referenced from over 120 published scientific studies and peer reviews. Those who refuse to believe the information in this book are free to check the references and point out any fallacies in the European researchers' reports.

Speaking of references, if you see a scientific study referenced with the words et al. after the main researchers name this just means additional researchers were part of the study as well. In science, there's a lot of jargon and I try my best to breakdown the jargon so that anyone can read and understand the language. Doctors, physicians, medics and scientists all use the same type of language, so understanding the jargon is crucial to understanding melanin. Nowadays scientists are developing bad reputations due to highly publicized cases of scientific misconduct, data fraud and funding bias (supporting the interests of the study's financial sponsor). This is why I must make it clear from the start that I am not a laboratory scientist, political scientist, social scientist, geneticist, biologist, chemist or physicist. Although my students call me "The Scientist", I am not a real scientist at all. I am simply someone who wants to know the truth about melanin. And if we're being honest, you are too! So let's begin.

CONTENTS

INTRODUCTION   10

Acknowledgements 11

Who am I? 11

Follow Logic 12

What is science? 13

Elementary Knowledge 14

WHAT IS MELANIN?   18

Scientist Findings 18

Photosynthesis 21

Cellular Respiration 21

Melanin > Chlorophyll.. 22

Conclusion... 23

Melanin Quiz 1 26

DIFFERENT TYPES OF MELANIN   28

Eumelanin and Pheomelanin 31

Neuromelanin 33

Substantia Nigra.. 35

Locus Coeruleus 36

Melanin Quiz 2 38

EMBRYOGENESIS   41

Gastrulation 41

Embryogenesis Summary 44

Melanin Quiz 3 47

THE IMPORTANCE OF PIGMENTS   49

Photopigments / Visual Pigments.. 49

Melanopsin 49

Rhodopsin 50

Plant Pigments 51

Heme Pigments 52

Pigments in Biology 54

The Electromagnetic Spectrum 57

How We See Colour 58

Melanin Quiz 4 62

MELANOGENESIS 65

Pineal Gland 66

Circadian Rhythm 67

Melanogenesis Regulators 69

Light and Melatonin 69

Eyesight and Melanogenesis 71

Blue Light Emission 72

Social Media, Streaming Services and Sleep 73

Melanogenesis Inhibition 74

Melanogenesis Step-By-Step 74

Internal & External Regulators 75

Melanogenesis and Sunscreen 76

Melanin Quiz 5 78

FOODS FOR MELANIN 81

Full Spectrum 81

Resveratrol 82

Selenium 82

PUFA's Omega 6 and 3 83

Amino Acids 85

Copper 87

Caution 88

Foods for Eumelanin 89

Foods for Pheomelanin 91

Melanin Quiz 6 93

WATER FOR MELANIN 96

Structured Water 96

Fourth Phase of Water 98

What Creates Structured Water? 100

Unstructured Water 101

Alkaline Water 102

Unstructured Environments 103

Pseudoscience vs Common Sense 104

Structured Water Properties 104

Water Discoveries of the Past 105

Dr. Mona Harrison 106

Bioavailable Water Characteristics 107

Melanin Quiz 7 109

MELANIN CONFUSION 112

Confusing Children About Melanin 113

Confusion Leads to Conflict 113

Sunlight Confusion 116

Sun Block Confusion 116

Protection Confusion 118

Skin Confusion 119

Carbon Confusion 119

Dark Universe Confusion 123

Black Light Confusion...127

Melanin Quiz 8 129

MELANIN DECODED 132

It has a broad absorption spectrum 132

It's a semiconductor.. 133

It's a powerful antioxidant... 133

It's an energy transducer.. 136

It's ubiquitous... 137

Melanin dissociates the water molecule into hydrogen and oxygen 138

Melanin Quiz 9 142

CODE OF SILENCE 144

Benefits of UV Radiation 144

Vitamin D Code of Silence 145

Vitamin D Supplementation Code of Silence.................... 148

The Truth About Vitamin D 148

UV Light and Melanin Code of Silence............................. 149

The Elephant in the Room... 150

Space Travel Code of Silence 150

Henrietta Lacks Code of Silence 151

Bioelectronics Code of Silence.. 153

Melanin Quiz 10 154

MELANIN AND MARIJAUNA   157

Drug Testing 157

A Secret System.. 159

The Endocannabinoid System (ECS)................................. 160

Benefits of CBD 162

Foods For ECS.. 163

Phytocannabinoids 164

Exercise and Endocannabinoids 165

Sex, Reproduction and Endocannabinoids 166

Melanogenesis and Endocannabinoids............................. 168

ECS Code of Silence.. 169

Melanin Quiz 11.. 171

PSEUDOSCIENCE OF MELANIN   174

Melanists and Afrocentricity... 175

Research and References.. 177

The Evidence is You!.. 177

Science of Self 178

On Earth 179

REFERENCES   180

ANSWERS   191

ANSWERS 192

MARSHALL'S MELANIN TIPS   194

P.O.W.E.R.S Defined.. 194

Human Energy Powered by Nature..................................... 197

P.O.W.E.R.S Poster.. 198

INDEX   199

ABOUT THE AUTHOR   206

INTRODUCTION

"Melanin drippin"... "melanin poppin"... "melanin on fleek"... "melanin magic"...I've heard these terms quite frequently over the years by many people who say they are proud of their skin colour and are simply expressing a love for their complexion. On social media this expression of love is shown in many ways with users tagging their posts with various hashtags relating to melanin, like #melaninqueen, #melaninking, #melaninbeauty, #melaninglowin' and #melaninpower to name a few. Despite all of this talk about melanin, it still seems to be a subject that is shrouded in mystery. Even our most knowledgeable scholars can't fully agree on what melanin is or what it does.

For example, the master teacher Dr. Llaila Afrika once said that melanin is the chemical key to life and is produced by the pineal gland. Minister EnQi SangReal (currently known as Dr. EnQi) once said that melanin is not produced by the pineal gland, but agrees it is very important to all living organisms. Professor Carol Barnes in his book *Melanin: The Chemical Key To Black Greatness* states that Melanin has chemical and physical properties which distinguish it from other chemicals and is so fantastic it may be considered "DIVINE." However, the late great Dr. Sebi once said controversially that there's no such thing as melanin... "it's carbon!"

So, what's the truth?!

What is melanin? What does it do? And is it even important? These are questions that I will explore in a very simplified way, to ensure you finish reading this book with a total understanding of melanin and its properties. It really excites me to be sharing these discoveries about melanin with you that could radically transform the way you view science, yourself and life in general. The information in this book changed my life forever and gave me a thorough knowledge of self that I never thought possible. Many of us go through life lost and confused, not knowing who we are or why we are here. This confusion stems from a lack of identity, miseducation and no knowledge of self. If we are being honest, we all know very little of ourselves, our reality and our true potential. Consciousness seeks to know itself. And thus, you find yourself reading this book seeking answers to life's dark mysteries. Becoming more self-aware is an on-going spiritual journey. It involves an intentional focus on self. When many of us embark on this spiritual journey we tend to pick up books that teach us about our history. And rightly so, as a wise man once said, "A people without the knowledge of their past history, origin and culture is like a tree without roots." Understanding who you are by learning about the past is extremely important. However, I always find it interesting when individuals go on a self-discovery journey by learning about their cultural and spiritual past, yet they neglect to learn about their physical and biological present. Why would knowledge of self not include your physical self? Your physical body is like a divine vehicle, equipped with everything you need to navigate you through life's experiences. And like any other vehicle you own, you need to know how it works in order to operate and take care of it. This is why I can't tell you how excited I am to be imparting this knowledge unto you. I feel honoured to be able to share what I know to help people understand themselves more, from a science perspective. I truly believe this information could transform your life for the better, as it has mine. So I thank you for allowing me to reveal what I have discovered about melanin with you in this book. I hope you find it useful.

Acknowledgements

On that note, I must pause to thank all the melanin scholars who came before me and left behind powerful books and lectures that I've learnt from and continue to learn from to this day. Firstly, I'd like to thank Dr. Llaila Afrika; to me the master teacher, who has written many books on melanin. You were one of the first teachers to open my eyes to the science of melanin. I had the pleasure of meeting you in 2018 and the words of wisdom you left me with will resonate with me forever. I thank you for helping me to understand melanin and giving me words of encouragement to continue to pursue my passion. Dr. Richard King, one of the godfathers of melanin research. I thank you for leading the way during a time where no one wanted to step forward and tell the absolute truth about melanin in all its existence. Dr. Frances Cress Welsing, words cannot express my appreciation for the work you have left us with. Your work gave me a thorough understanding as to why this information is hidden from the masses. Thank you Dr. Welsing. There are many more I could thank but these three started the journey for me; the journey into darkness, the journey into the unknown, where some of the mysteries of the world have been hiding. Let's delve deep into these dark secrets and see what we can find. Are you ready to venture with me down the rabbit hole? I wonder...

Who am I?

Now before we delve in, allow me to introduce myself: My name is Leon Marshall. I'm a sports science lecturer and fitness course tutor at London South Bank University. I have worked at various Universities in and around London, including Imperial College London and Middlesex University. My speciality is Anatomy & Physiology as I love exploring how the human body works. At Imperial College London I was chosen to be one of their Expert Childhood Obesity Trainers. For nearly a decade, between 2011 and 2019, we would go into primary schools in the South London area and train the teachers, the pupils and sometimes the parents about the dangers of childhood obesity; which has become a very big problem in the UK. Teaching children about health and how the body works was very rewarding for me and I cherished every moment of it. I discovered that teaching children made me a better teacher of science; because I had to make sure the children understood the complexities of the human body in a very simplified way. If I was explaining to them what vitamins and minerals do and why they are important I'd make sure to use words and language they understood. If I was explaining anything scientific to them I would use analogies from their own life experiences so they could relate to it straight away. By doing this with the children over and over again this quickly became my style of teaching science to anyone, young or old. So whether I'm presenting a lecture in front of 300 students at a University or talking to a school assembly full of children aged 5-10 years old, I teach science in exactly the same way: simplistically.

"Simplicity is the key to brilliance" -Bruce Lee

"The language of truth is simple" -Euripides

These are two of my favourite quotes and as a seeker of truth they both resonate with me. I have been a seeker of truth all my life and a teacher of science for over 15 years; and what I've found is that science is the best route to the truth. So my internal GPS is always navigating me towards science. If you haven't already guessed it, Science is my passion. Science of the body, science of the mind, science of the universe, science of life. But it hasn't always been this way. I used to hate science (with a passion!). I look back at times and wonder why? Maybe it was the fact that all my science teachers made the subject so confusing, so boring, so complex or just so unclear. Whatever the reason, it was not something I liked to study.

That all changed when I first got introduced to melanin. I was given a book called *The Isis Papers* by Dr. Frances Cress Welsing in my early twenties. Before reading that book I had no idea what melanin actually was. I was then given another book to read called *Nutricide* by Dr. Llaila Afrika. In that book he states that there are 12 melanin centers in the brain. He also claims that melanin, secreted by the pineal gland, stimulates the repair of cells, tissues and organs. It acts as an antibiotic, enhances immunity, converts sunlight energy (vitamin D), stimulates DNA synthesis, influences lymphocyte production and increases sound and light absorption. When I was reading this I was like, "Wow, is all of that true?! This melanin thing sounds amazing!!" I've heard the saying that if something sounds too good to be true, it probably is. However, I don't follow sayings, statements or superstitions to get to the truth. I follow logic.

Follow Logic

As a scientist I like to investigate things thoroughly in order to get total clarity on whatever I'm studying. I have found that the best way to get total clarity on anything scientific is to gather evidence and follow the logic. Why follow logic? Because logic came with the universe. I learnt that from another powerful scholar by the name of Neely Fuller Jr. He believes the universe was made in a logical way, so if we follow logic we are following universal guidance. The more I study the universe the more I realise this to be true. So then, what is logic? There are many definitions out there that one could memorise, but according to Neely Fuller Jr. if a definition of a word doesn't make total sense to you or doesn't work for you, you have a God-given right to make up your own definition. So to me, logic is just common sense. Common sense is something we all have, whether we use it or not. It's like an intuitive gift that we are all born with. And it's up to us to utilise it to help us navigate our way through life and be problem solvers. Why do we need to be problem solvers? Because we will all encounter problems throughout our life that need to be solved. Using logic and common sense will serve you well when you encounter these problems. By tapping into your own logic of how the universe works and using common sense to solve problems you may find that the solution to the problem is quite simple. For example, if I was to ask you what's 2+2? I'm hoping your common sense would kick in and you'd say 4. You don't need to be taught this, because you can verify it yourself using your own fingers. You can then gather evidence to see what other people got. "Hey, I did it on my fingers and I got 4. You try it. What did you get?" If someone tells you they got 7 and not 4, that's absolutely fine because all they would need to do to prove that 2+2 = 7 is show you how they got to 7. Problem solved. Applying this same logical approach to scientific problems makes science simple.

What is science?

Now as this book will focus heavily on the science of melanin, it makes sense to start with a definition of science that is easy to understand. So I present to you my very own definition:

"Science is logic backed up by evidence"

In other words, science is nothing but common sense, backed up with proof. The proof should be replicable over and over again. Just like 2+2. Common sense says the answer is always 4. But to make it scientific all you need to do is... prove it! You can prove it in many ways, using your own fingers or with pens, fruits, cars, people or planets. 2+2 is 4 everywhere on planet Earth, in any situation or any context. This makes science very simple to understand, because it takes it away from being this thing that only 'smart' people get, to it being just simple maths. With that being said, this book will explain what melanin is in a very simplified way to ensure that everyone can follow along without any confusion. I pride myself on teaching science this way because a wise man once said:

"If you can't explain it simply, you don't understand it well enough."

That was Albert Einstein, who's widely considered one of the greatest scientists of all time. I agree with this statement, but I'd take it one step further and say, "If you can't explain it simply, you don't understand it well enough. Or you do, you just don't want me to understand it." This means that if someone is teaching you science in a complex convoluted way, they're either confused about the subject themselves, or they are trying to confuse you. Why else wouldn't they just explain it simply?

"Science is Simple" –Leon Marshall

This is my quote and I stand by it firmly. Science is very simple to understand, because it's just logic and evidence. I know what you're thinking. If science is so simple Leon, then what on Earth is melanin and why are we all so confused about it? I have created this book for that very reason: To end all the confusion surrounding melanin. For the select few who believe they are not confused about melanin; you know, the "know-it-alls," I have one thing to say to you (using my best Kevin Hart voice), "You gon' learn today!"

Elementary Knowledge

Before you start Chapter One there are some basic concepts and terms to be aware of. Look at the periodic table of elements. You may remember this table from science class back in your school days (if you weren't sleeping in class like me!). It lists all the elements known to man and is used as a reference point when talking about atoms. See if you can spot some of the most common elements on the table. Like Carbon, Hydrogen, Oxygen and Nitrogen. Notice the atomic number associated with these atoms. What is the atomic number of carbon? This information will serve you well as you work your way through this book. Coming up are some elementary (fundamental) terms that will help you understand the science you are about to learn. Keep these in your mental rolodex and refer back to them throughout the book. Enjoy the journey!

Elementary Terms that will help you throughout this book:

Atom: the smallest unit of matter that forms a chemical element, consisting of protons, neutrons and electrons

Protons: positively charged subatomic particles of an atom, found within the nucleus of the atom.

Neutron: subatomic particles of an atom which have a neutral charge (not positive or negative), found within the nucleus of the atom.

Electrons: negatively charged subatomic particles of an atom, found orbiting the atom.

Electricity: the flow (or movement) of electrons

Conductor: a material or substance that allows electrons to flow freely through it. Conductors facilitate electricity

"The body is electric" –Dr Sebi

Periodic Table of the Elements

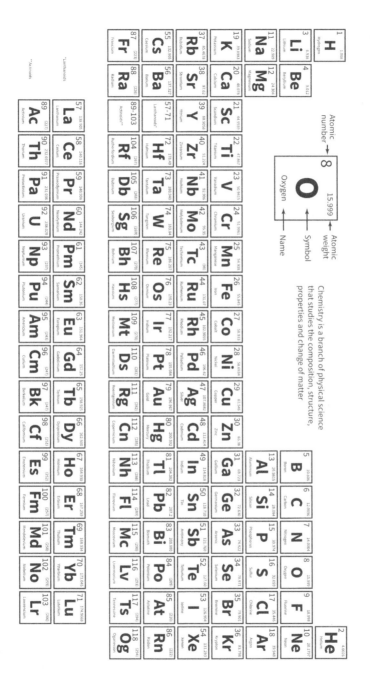

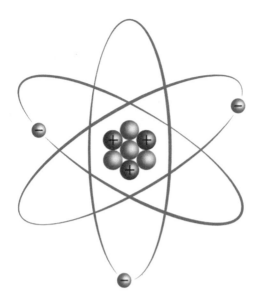

Atom structure
+ Proton
● Neutron
⊖ Electron

KNOW THYSELF
MELANIN $C_{18}H_{10}N_2O_4$

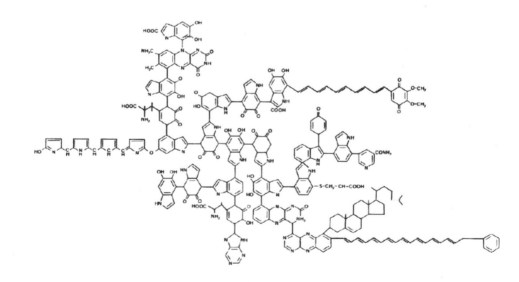

16

Chapter One

WHAT IS MELANIN?

WHAT IS MELANIN?

"Melanin is the Chemical Key To Life" –Dr Llaila O. Afrika

There are many scientists who have done extensive research on melanin. They have published papers, written books, presented information on it or examined it in a laboratory setting. As I am not a "real" scientist it would be naïve for me to think I know more about melanin than the true qualified scientists who have studied it prior to me. So with that being said, I'm going to present to you five different scientists who have all reviewed this mysterious dark pigment and shared publically what they have found. Once I've presented all five scientists' findings, I'll allow you to put two and two together and see what you get.

Scientist Findings

Scientist #1 - Dr. T. Owens Moore, Ph.D.

In his book *The Science & Myth of Melanin* Dr. T. Owens Moore states that Melanin is more than just a pigment and is found in many areas of the body besides the skin. I have summarised and bullet pointed some of his findings.

According to Dr. T. Owens Moore

- In humans, melanin is the primary determinant of skin and hair colour
- Melanin has genetic, biochemical and functional links to the immune system
- It neutralizes toxic substances and free radicals
- Found in almost every organ of the body and is necessary for the brain and nerves to operate, the eyes to see and the cells to reproduce
- Also found in the stria vascularis of the inner ear
- Melanin is strategically located in areas of the body where energy conversion or charge transfer occurs
- It helps to prevent DNA damage in cells
- There are many types of melanin: cosmo melanin, eumelanin, pheomelanin and neuro melanin (to name a few)

Scientist #2 - Dr. Karl Maret

Karl Maret, M.D., holds degrees in electrical and biomedical engineering. He has been a life-long student in the field of subtle energy and Energy Medicine. In an infamous online video this doctor proceeds to break down melanin in quite some detail. Here's a bullet point summary of what he says about melanin.

According to Dr Karl Maret

- It's 'The Chemical Key To Life'
- Melanin has a broad absorption spectrum
- Absorbs thousands of times more electromagnetic radiation (photons) than chlorophyll
- Melanin is an important energy regulating molecule in the body

- Exists in many tissues besides the skin
- Is present in developing foetus
- Thought to be a master molecule for steering biological processes in the body
- Health effects still being researched

Scientist #3 - Dr. Richard King

Richard D. King (Died: December 16, 2013) was a psychiatrist, historian, and melanin/pineal gland scholar. He was most widely known for his influential studies of Melanin and Ancient Kemet. He is the author of African Origin of Biological Psychiatry, Melanin: Key To Freedom, and The Black Dot.

According to Dr Richard King

- There are 4 major broad sub sections of the "Melanin Life Ocean"
  (i) Cosmic Melanin
  (ii) Planetary Melanin
  (iii) Plant Kingdom Melanin
  (iv)Animal Kingdom Melanin.

- Found throughout the entire body of all humans in their skin, eyes, endocrine glands, blood, heart, muscles, lungs, gastrointestinal tract, kidney/urogenital tract, sexual organs and the brain
- Melanin in the brain is called Neuromelanin
- Within the human brain stem are twelve centers of black melanin, including Locus Coeruleus and Substantia Nigra
- Melanin is critical to hearing. African people hear a wider range of sound than Europeans, in particular the low bass sounds
- Melanin in the skin comes in two types: Eumelanin and Pheomelanin

Scientist #4 - Mr. Carol Barnes (Senior Research Chemist)

In his book "MELANIN: The Chemical Key To Black Greatness" Mr. Carol Barnes states that Melanin was once considered by "western scientists" to be a "waste" product of body metabolism and serves no useful function within the body. He then goes onto prove how false this claim was with evidence of what melanin truly does within the human body.

According to Mr Carol Barnes

- Melanin is a refined, complex, multifunctional chemical that has a wide variety of important functions within the human body, and in the environment
- It is located in important areas of the nervous system and major organs throughout the body
- Melanin can also be found in our environment in places such as soil, plants, animals, and in the water of creeks, lakes, springs, seas and rivers
- Melanin has the ability to combine or chemically react with various drugs and chemicals

- Illegal drugs such as cocaine, LSD, marijuana, heroin, amphetamines etc alter or change melanin's chemical structure, electrical charge and electronic configuration, thus altering many life supporting activities
- The combining of melanin to harmful drugs means that those with higher levels of melanin are more likely to become addicted to drugs and stay addicted longer

Scientist #5 - Dr. Auturo Solis Herrera

Auturo Solis Herrera is a medical surgeon, othalmologist and pharmacologist. He does extensive research in the fields of Nutritional Biochemistry, Neurology and Clinical Pharmacology.

According to Dr. Auturo Solis Herrera

- Melanin is to the animal kingdom what chlorophyll is to the plant kingdom
- Herrera called melanin a "super chlorophyll" due to its many advantages over regular chlorophyll
- Found that it exists in many tissues besides the skin
- Found that the intrinsic property of melanin is to dissociate (split) the water molecule, like chlorophyll in plants.
- Wrote a book about it called "The Human Photosynthesis"

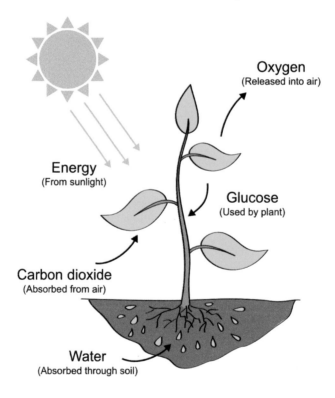

*Figure 1 - **Photosynthesis***

The Human Photosynthesis? Wait..?! Is he saying that melanin can do what plants do during photosynthesis? This would be a huge paradigm shift and quantum leap in melanin research if it were found to be true. Let's remind ourselves of what we were all taught in school about photosynthesis.

Photosynthesis

Photosynthesis is the process used by plants, algae and certain bacteria to turn sunlight, carbon dioxide (CO^2) and water into food (glucose) and oxygen (O^2). Chlorophyll is the green pigment in leaves that helps plants absorb and utilize light energy from the sun to make food. A byproduct of this process is oxygen, which the plant freely releases into the air.

Here's a simplified way of looking at photosynthesis:

Water + Carbon Dioxide + Sunlight (reactants) = Oxygen + Glucose (products)

The two products of photosynthesis (oxygen and glucose) are very important to the cellular health of human beings. In each of our cells there's a set of chemical reactions that results in energy production. This process is called Cellular Respiration.

Cellular Respiration

Cellular Respiration is the process by which your cells use glucose and oxygen to make Carbon Dioxide, Water and Adenosine Triphosphate (ATP), which we've been taught is the energy currency of the cell.

Here's a simplified way of looking at cellular respiration:

Glucose + Oxygen (reactants) = Carbon Dioxide + Water + ATP (products)

Do you notice any similarities between this equation and the photosynthesis one? Take another look at the photosynthesis equation and you'll notice that both equations are inversely identical. In other words, the products of photosynthesis (glucose and oxygen) are what humans need for cellular respiration. And the products of cellular respiration (carbon dioxide and water) are what plants need for photosynthesis. One could argue that this reveals a symbiotic relationship between us and plants. What the plants breathe out (oxygen), we breathe in. And what we breathe out (carbon dioxide), the plants breathe in.

If Dr. Auturo Solis Herrera is correct, a long-standing assumption that only plants are capable of utilising light energy directly is thrown out the window. In other words,

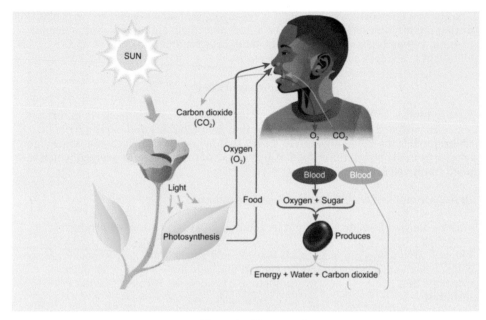

*Figure 2 - **Plants and us***

melanin may be capable of ingesting sunlight, and like plants, using the harvested light in biologically useful ways. One of the main things it does biologically, according to Dr. Herrera, is split the water molecule into hydrogen and oxygen. When I read this in his book I was blown away. In regards to how humans produce energy, this changes everything! Hydrogen is the cleanest primary energy source we have on Earth. If melanin is able to separate hydrogen from the water molecule, then the hydrogen could be used to power chemical processes in the body. I couldn't find any other scientists supporting this claim however, so the validity of this statement doesn't have much support.

Melanin > Chlorophyll

Dr. Herrera truly believes that melanin is analogous to chlorophyll, and he claims he has proven that melanin can perform the first key step in photosynthesis: the splitting of the water molecule into hydrogen and oxygen. Everyone is taught about photosynthesis at school, a process that could not be possible without chlorophyll absorbing electromagnetic radiation from the sun. This is something all children are taught from a young age, and for good reason. Photosynthesis is one of the most fundamental processes on our planet. It is essential that all children are taught this process to understand the environment they live in, the food they eat and the air they breathe. Hence, the necessary inclusion of this information in most school curriculums. What seems to be excluded however, is real information on melanin. Dr. Auturo Solis Herrera calls melanin a "super chlorophyll" due to its many advantages over regular chlorophyll. This is backed up by Dr. Karl Maret's findings which show that melanin can absorb thousands of times more electromagnetic radiation than chlorophyll. So children in most schools are taught about a pigment that exists in plants but not taught about a pigment that exists in their skin. I'm curious, why do you think that is?

Conclusion

What can we conclude about melanin based on the research of these five distinguished scientists mentioned above? Here's what all five scientists agree on:

- Melanin is not just in the skin
- It exists in many organs and tissues including the brain
- Melanin in the brain is called neuromelanin
- There are different types of melanin
- It is a powerful antioxidant
- It can repair DNA
- It's very efficient at absorbing light

The main consensus around melanin is its ability to absorb light and utilise this energy internally. All five scientists mention this characteristic in their work. Another doctor whose findings are in accordance with these five scientists when it comes to what melanin can do is Dr. Frank Barr. He and his colleagues published a famous scientific paper about melanin in 1983 entitled *Melanin: The organising molecule* [1]. This was a very controversial scientific paper at the time it was published, because most of the research around melanin prior to 1983 had been hidden from public view. In the paper, Dr. Frank Barr and his colleagues established that:

- Melanin is an ancient pigment which was present at the inception of "life" and which appears to have a nearly ubiquitous distribution within and among living organisms
- Melanin appears to possess the most diverse functional properties of all light-absorbing molecules.
- It can absorb light and sound in the form of music
- Melanin exhibits extraordinary binding properties for aromatic and lipid-soluble compounds
- (neuro)melanin (in conjunction with other pigment molecules such as the isopentenoids) functions as the major organizational molecule in living systems.
- (neuro)melanin is capable of self-synthesis.
- Melanin is an extremely efficient light (photon) absorbing molecule, exhibiting extraordinary photon-phonon conversion processes.
- Melanin continuously produces functionally active free radicals and, in addition, is a scavenger of free radicals
- Melanin is a remarkable oxidation-reduction polymer, able to simultaneously oxidize one substance while reducing another
- Melanin transduces both acoustic and electric energy fields and it can generate enough heat to effect metabolic processes.
- In addition to responding functionally to both light and sound and being abundant in both eyes and inner ears, melanin and neuro-melanin (the form of melanin found in the central nervous system) is located in highly strategic

functional regions of the central and peripheral nervous system (including the midbrain reticular formation, substantia nigra and locus coeruleus)

- Melanin functions as an amorphous semiconductor within physiological ranges of neuronal electrical potentials
- Electronic processing in neuronal systems may be effectively triggered by as little as one photon or by an auditory (phononic) input

That was a lot of scientific jargon, which can get confusing to the average person who's not familiar with the terminologies used. The confusing jargon used in science is something I will discuss later. But for now, just notice how they emphasise melanin's ability to absorb light *and* sound. Anytime you see the word photon in science they are talking about light. Anytime you see the word phonon in science they are talking about sound. So, where it says that melanin exhibits extraordinary photon-phonon conversion processes, this means that it doesn't just absorb light, it can convert that light into sound. Studies have shown that melanin can even do the reverse and convert sound into light as well. Conversion seems to be one of melanin's strong points. But not just conversion, another strong point emphasised by Dr. Frank Barr et al. is its organizing capabilities. According to their findings, this "organising molecule" is capable of organising the elements of the whole living system (organism). Here's an excerpt from the paper of what it means to organise a system.

> *"To organize a system is to arrange or form its elements into a coherent, functional whole. How such organization takes place within living systems such as the cell remains a central question of biological research."*

To organize implies putting things in systematic order so that the whole system works as a unit. Each element inside the unit must be organized in their functions in order for the whole system to operate optimally. Where would the energy come from for such organisation to take place? Logically speaking, anything that needs organising requires energy. If your bedroom is untidy and needs organising, you will have to do whatever's necessary to tidy up your room. The room isn't going to tidy itself. It requires work, your work, your energy. So where does melanin get this energy from to 'tidy up' so to speak? According to the scientists mentioned above it seems to be from absorbing light and sound. It is believed that melanin doesn't just absorb light and sound frequencies; studies show that it is capable of absorbing, storing and utilising all types of electromagnetic energy. It can even absorb harmful frequencies and transform them into useful energy. In other words, whatever energy melanin is supplied with it has an uncanny ability to use this energy to help organise the living system. Isn't that fascinating?

That's the end of chapter one. How was it for you? We've only just scratched the surface of what melanin can do and there's so much more to reveal. But before we delve even deeper, let's take a moment to reflect on what you just read.

Quiz Time

At the end of each chapter there will be a melanin quiz to test your understanding of what you've just read. Each quiz will have multiple choice questions for you to answer. There's only one correct answer for each question; so this is a great way for you to evaluate yourself and see how much melanin knowledge you are absorbing. Answers to all quizzes can be found at the back of the book. Use each quiz to test yourself, your friends and your family members to ensure this knowledge spreads far and wide. Good luck!

Melanin Quiz 1 – What is Melanin?

1 According to Dr. Llaila Afrika and Dr. Karl Maret, melanin is
- A. The Chemical Key To Destruction
- B. The Chemical Key To Depression
- C. The Chemical Key To Death
- D. The Chemical Key To Life

2 What did Dr. T. Owens Moore say about melanin?
- A. Melanin is the primary determinant of skin and hair colour
- B. Melanin has genetic, biochemical and functional links to the immune system
- C. Melanin helps to prevent DNA damage in cells
- D. All the above

3 According to Dr. Richard King, how many centres of Black Melanin (neuromelanin) are there in the brain?
- A. 2
- B. 12
- C. 22
- D. 200

4 Dr. Auturo Solis Herrera found that the intrinsic property of melanin is
- A. To disassociate (split) CO^2 into Carbon and Oxygen
- B. To disassociate (split) NH^3 into Nitrogen and Hydrogen
- C. To disassociate (split) H^2O into Hydrogen and Oxygen
- D. To disassociate (split) bun and cheese into rice and peas

5 Why are plants vitally important to human life and vice versa?
- A. Plants breathe out oxygen, humans breathe it in
- B. Humans breathe out carbon dioxide, plants breathe it in
- C. A + B
- D. Plants are not important to human life

6 In the 1983 published paper entitled: *Melanin: The organizing molecule* Dr. Frank Barr et al. reported that melanin can
- A. Absorb Light
- B. Absorb Sound (music)
- C. Organise Living Systems
- D. All the above

CHAPTER TWO

DIFFERENT TYPES OF MELANIN

DIFFERENT TYPES OF MELANIN

Every human being on planet Earth has melanin. However, there are different types of melanin that can vary in each of us.

Types of Melanin

In humans, melanin exists as three forms:

- **EUMELANIN** (black and / or brown form)
- **PHEOMELANIN** (red and / or yellow form)
- **NEUROMELANIN** (form found in the brain and nervous system)

Other types of melanin include:

- **ALLOMELANIN**
- **PLANT MELANIN**
- **FUNGAL MELANIN**
- **BACTERIAL MELANIN**
- **SYNTHETIC MELANIN**

The name "melanin" comes from the ancient Greek *melanos*, meaning "black" or "dark." This information is taken from a review article published in the New Journal of Science entitled: *Melanins: Skin Pigments and Much More—Types, Structural Models, Biological Functions, and Formation Routes* [2]

> *"Melanin is the generic name used to refer to perhaps the most ubiquitous, resistant, heterogeneous, and ancient pigments found in nature. Melanin appeared very early in most living kingdoms on the Earth. Thus, melanin has been recently found in very old fossils from dinosaurs, early birds, nonavian theropod species, and primitive cephalopods. These recent findings will probably make melanin a new biomarker in life evolution."*

This extract sounds very scientific and some of the words used went over my head the first time I read them. Learning science can sometimes be a laborious task, due to all the technical terminology. Not to worry though, I've gone through all the arduous hours, days, months and years of breaking down the language so you don't have to. After you finish reading this book you'll be able to explain what melanin is and what it does very simply to anyone who's interested in gaining this knowledge.

Ubiquitous

adjective
1. present, appearing, or found everywhere.
   "his ubiquitous influence was felt by all the family"

Heterogeneous

adjective
1.   CHEMISTRY
     of or denoting a process involving substances in different phases (solid,
     liquid, or gaseous).
     "heterogeneous catalysis"

When you see the word 'ubiquitous' and 'heterogeneous' being used to describe
melanin this simply means that melanin is found in all living organisms in various
forms, whether it be solid, liquid or gas. Hair, skin and eye colour in humans and in
animals is mainly determined by the amount and type of melanin they have. In
humans, melanin is produced by cells in the innermost layer of the skin (the basal
layer) and hair follicles called melanocytes. According to current-day science all
humans have the same amount of melanocytes in their skin and hair. If this is true,
then what causes us to have different colour hair and skin?

Melanocytes contain tiny organelles called melanosomes where melanin is
synthesised and stored. When the melanocytes are stimulated by a group of
hormones called Melanocyte Stimulating Hormones (MSH) to release melanin it is the
melanosomes, which are filled with melanin, that actually get released into the
epidermis (keratinocytes) and the hair. So the differences in skin and hair
pigmentation we see in humans are the result of the melanosomes size, distribution
and type of melanin produced within it. The type is either going to be eumelanin or
pheomelanin. This is determined by genes and the pH inside of the melanosome [3].
There are many different genes involved in this process, but the main gene
responsible for this is called melanocortin 1 receptor or MC1R. The term "pH" stands
for potential of hydrogen or power of hydrogen, and it indicates the acidity level or
alkalinity level of a water solution. Pure water is supposed to be neutral, so it should
have a pH score of 7. Anything below 7 is considered acidic and anything above 7 is
considered a basic solution or alkaline. Studies have shown that low melanosome pH
favours pheomelanin and high melanosome pH favours eumelanin [4].

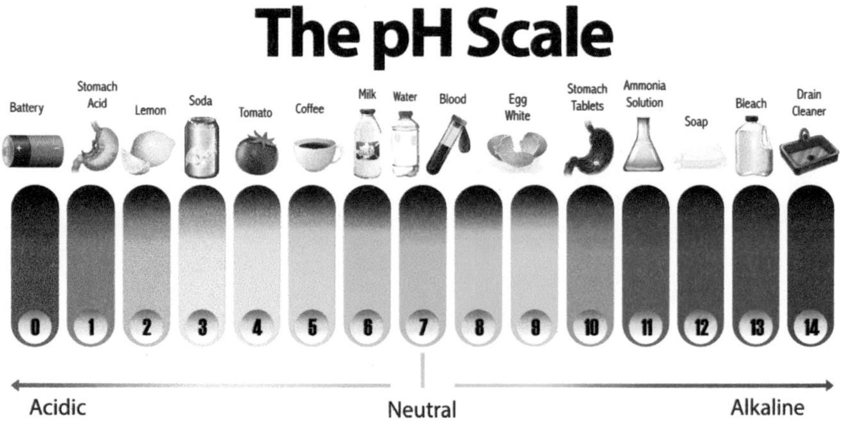

*Figure 3 - **PH scale***

29

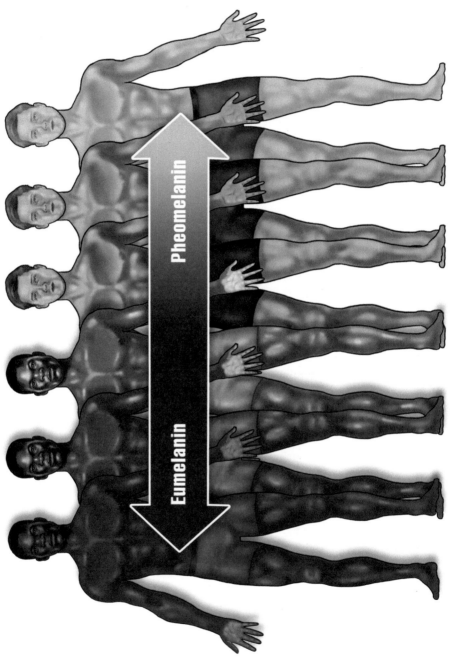

Figure 4 - Eumelanin to pheomelanin

30

Eumelanin and Pheomelanin

Pheomelanin (*sometimes spelt: phaeomelanin*) is a reddish to yellow sulphur-containing melanin pigment found in the presence of cysteine. It is responsible for the yellow (blond), pink to red hues seen in humans who have high amounts present. Individuals who are pheomelanin dominant usually have high amounts in their hair (red heads), lips, nipples, vaginal epithelium, and glans penis. Their skin tone might have a pinkish hue to it. Pheomelanin and Eumelanin are synthesised within melanosomes of melanocytes by a series of chemical reactions starting with the amino acid tyrosine. This process is called melanogenesis, a multistep process which begins with the conversion of tyrosine to DOPAquinone. Dopaquinone acts as a precursor to melanin and the neurotransmitter dopamine (hence the emphasis put on DOPA). It is interesting to note that the step-by-step process of producing dopamine in the brain and eumelanin in the skin are very similar. As dopamine is linked to addiction, this supports the statement made by Mr Carol Barnes in his book MELANIN: *The Chemical Key To Black Greatness*, that those with higher levels of melanin are more likely to become addicted to drugs and stay addicted longer. Eumelanin and dopamine are products of the same process. The key enzyme in this process is a copper-based enzyme named tyrosinase. The more tyrosinase activity the more eumelanin is formed.

Pheomelanins are also made from the same tyrosine as eumelanins and the process is much the same with tyrosinase playing a key role. The melanocortin 1 receptor (MC1R) controls which type of melanin is produced by melanocytes. When the receptor is activated by MSH, it triggers a series of chemical reactions inside melanocytes that stimulate these cells to make eumelanin. If the receptor is not activated or is blocked, melanocytes make pheomelanin instead of eumelanin. The amount depends on tyrosinase activity. Factors such as age can have an effect on tyrosinase activity. As we get older tyrosinase activity increases. It is most active in middle age and thereafter decreases. This can be seen in older individuals whose hair starts turning grey and sometimes even their eye colour changing due to a lack of melanin production. The other factor that can affect tyrosinase activity is, as already mentioned, the pH level inside the melanosome. Modern melanosomes generally carry a mixture of both eumelanin and pheomelanin. Therefore, the marked spectrum of colour and diversity of patterns that we see in humans arises from the variation in the quantity, quality, and regional distribution of just two types of melanin pigment.

Eumelanin is a brown to black pigment that is the most common form of melanin. The more eumelanin you have the darker your skin and your hair. Research shows that black hair contains about 99% eumelanin, brown and blond hair 95% eumelanin, and red hair 67% eumelanin [C R Borges et al, 2001]. It has been hypothesized that the pH and cysteine level of melanosomes influences the phenotype of hair. As pH reduces, there is a progressive reduction in tyrosinase activity leading to increased pheomelanin and reddish or blonde hair [4,5]. A mutation in melanocortin-1 receptor (MC1R) gene causes auburn or red colour of hair. This mutation is seen usually in individuals of Northern Europe with less sun exposure [6,7]. A study in 2012 showed a recessive mutation in tyrosinase-related protein 1 (TYRP1) in people with blonde hair [11].

Dopamine

Neurotransmitter
Hormone

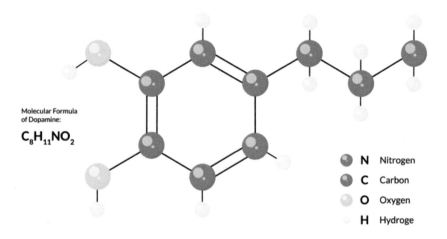

Structural Formula
of Dopamine:

Molecular Formula
of Dopamine:

$C_8H_{11}NO_2$

- **N** Nitrogen
- **C** Carbon
- **O** Oxygen
- **H** Hydroge

*Figure 5 - **Dopamine molecular structure***

Eumelanin and Pheomelanin Summary

- Melanocytes are melanin-producing cells found in skin, hair follicles, eyes, inner-ear, bones, heart and brain of humans
- Melanocytes (stimulated by MSH) produce either Eumelanin or Pheomelanin within tiny organelles called Melanosomes
- These melanosomes come in different shapes and sizes depending on the genetic makeup of the individual
- Pheomelanin melanosomes are generally small and oval, in contrast to the larger elongated shape of eumelanin-containing melanosomes [12].
- Both pheomelanin and eumelanin production start with the conversion of the amino acid tyrosine into dopaquinone
- This conversion is made possible by the activity of the copper-based enzyme called tyrosinase
- The melanocortin 1 receptor (MC1R) gene controls which type of melanin is produced by melanocytes
- When the receptor is activated, it triggers a series of chemical reactions inside melanocytes that stimulate these cells to make eumelanin
- If the receptor is not activated or is blocked, melanocytes make pheomelanin instead of eumelanin [6-10]

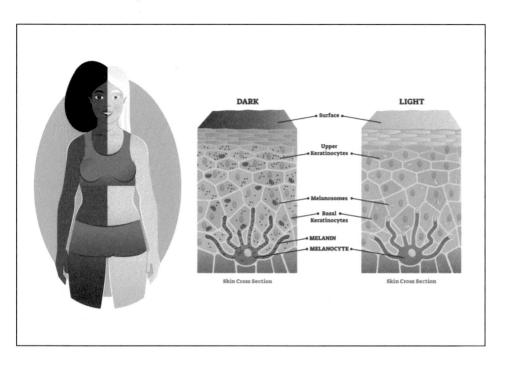

*Figure 6 - **Darkly Pigmented vs Lightly Pigmented***

Neuromelanin

Melanin is not just found in the skin. There is also a type of melanin called neuromelanin found in various parts of the brain. This neuromelanin affects how you taste food [13,14], hear sounds [15-24] and see colours [25]. Dr. Richard King in his book *MELANIN: A Key To Freedom*, states that melanin is critical to seeing light and hearing sounds. In one chapter entitled *MELANIN AND THE EYE*, he states that "without the melanin in the pigmented layer of the retina a life form will be permanently blind. Light vision is born from Blackness." In another chapter, entitled *MELANIN AND THE EAR* he lists various studies which have proven how important melanin is to hearing. Dozens of studies since have confirmed Dr. Kings' findings. The most notable of which being a study published by the Pigment Cell Research Journal (2006), in which the author concluded that sound needs sound melanocytes to be heard [26]. Make a mental note of that: In order for you to hear you need melanin in your ear. Light and sound frequencies are both interpreted by the brain, and neuromelanin's role in regulating these signals is scientifically proven. Within the human brain stem are twelve centers of black melanin:

(1) locus coeruleus
(2) substantia nigra
(3) nucleus parabrachialis
(4) nucleus paranigralis
(5) intracapularis subcerleus
(6) nervi trigeini

(7) mesencephasius
(8) pontis centralis oratis
(9) tegmenti pedennculopontis
(10) parabrachialis medialis
(11) medialis dorsomotor
(12) retro ambilgualis

These 12 Neuromelanin cell groups were first mapped by Olszewski and Baxter (1954) using the Nissi staining technique [27]. All animal life with a spinal column (vertebrates) have varying degrees of melanin pigmentation of these twelve centers, with the highest amounts being found in humans. So that means you, the powerful melanin-rich human being reading this book right now; yes you have 12 melanin-rich centers in your brain that controls the way you think, feel, touch, taste and see [17-27]. How amazing is that?

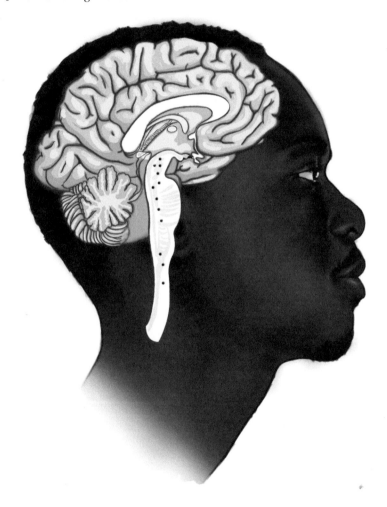

*Figure 7 - **Twelve Melanin Centers in the Brain***

34

When I first read about these twelve melanin-rich brain centers in Dr. Richard King's book I thought to myself, "Whoa! Is this true?! How come I've never heard of these 12 centers before?" I had been studying science for over 5 years before I stumbled across any information regarding neuromelanin. So I found it quite strange that this information was not widely known. I started to do lots of research on this topic to see what I could find. Turns out there's not much information at all about these twelve neuromelanin centers in any neuroscience books, neuroscience websites or videos online that discuss neurology. Why do you think that is? I've had previous university students tell me that they'd never heard of neuromelanin before. This may not seem so out of place until you realise what these students were actually studying. These university students were studying either neuropsychology, neurophysiology, neurology or they were doing a masters in neuroscience. In other words, they gained a degree in how the brain works and were never taught about the 12 black centers inside the brain that regulates how the brain works. Isn't that strange? Can you imagine studying neuroscience at a top UK University for 3-5 years and never being taught the main substance in the brain that controls your five senses? When these students told me how little they knew about neuromelanin it gave me a sense of purpose. This is valuable information for all human beings to know. The highest levels of neuromelanin are found in the neurons of the substantia nigra and locus coeruleus. These are two parts of the brain that everyone should know about. Let's examine them closer.

Substantia Nigra

In the center of the brain, at its base, is a structure known as the substantia nigra, which literally means "black substance" or a "substantial amount of blackness." This substance plays an important role in the regulation of human movements. In fact, it is responsible for a major part of what makes us human in terms of our behaviour and motor function. The substantia nigra gets its dark colouring from the large number of dopamine neurons within it, as they express high levels of the dark pigment neuromelanin. Dopamine is a neurotransmitter in the brain that plays several important roles in the brain and body. Mainly, dopamine is responsible for mediating our movements, memory, mood and motivation towards behaviours that lead to feelings of pleasure. The release of dopamine creates a reward circuit in the brain. This circuit registers an intense experience (such as taking drugs, having sex or eating food) as "important" and creates lasting memories of it as pleasurable. It is directly linked to our reward-motivated behaviours and could explain why people become addicted to certain detrimental behaviours. Most of the dopamine neurons in the brain are found in the substantia nigra. Smooth coordinated movement is such a major function of the substantia nigra that a diminished substantia nigra leads to parkinsons disease [28]. Studies have also shown that it can impact alzheimer's disease [29]. Dysfunction of the substantia nigra may also lead to schizophrenia and/or addictive behaviour due to dopamine.

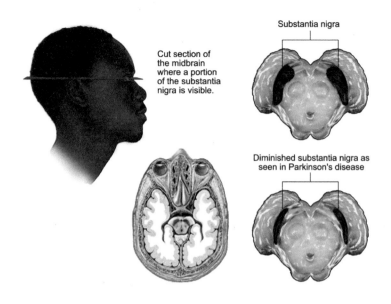

Cut section of the midbrain where a portion of the substantia nigra is visible.

Substantia nigra

Diminished substantia nigra as seen in Parkinson's disease

*Figure 8 - **Substantia nigra***

Locus Coeruleus

The Locus Coeruleus (LC) is located in the brainstem and a branch of the Reticular activating system. One of its functions is controlling the panic and Stress Response [30]. LC is the major source of the Norepinephrine (noradrenaline) along with adrenal medulla which supplies the Norepinephrine directly to the blood [31]. Together with adrenaline, norepinephrine increases heart rate and blood pumping from the heart as a response to arousal, vigilance and attention. The colour of the LC is dark blue to black due to the melanin or pigmented cells inside the neurons of the LC. It is believed that there is a link between the LC and many neural pathologies such as Alzheimer, Parkinson and depression. According to Dr. Richard King, the LC is the one brain center deeply pigmented with black melanin that only exists in humans, therefore it is absent in other primates. Here's an excerpt from his book where he describes what he calls "the Black Dot".

"The Locus Coeruleus literally means, Black Dot. Locus is a Latin word, stlocus locum, meaning point or dot. Coeruleus is a Sanskrit word, caerleus yamas, meaning black. The philosophical concept of the Black Dot is a key concept found at the core of ancient African Systems of Knowledge such as the ancient Annu hieroglyphic name for Khui Land, the Great Lakes site of the birth place of humanity and the Egyptian hieroglyphic name for sun god Ra. This is profound evidence that ancient Africans studied brain anatomy and named this brain site Black Dot because its appearance and function revealed evidence of a symbolism, chemistry, anatomy, and history that was in line with then known research evidence of the role of Black Melanin throughout nature."

From an African-centred perspective, Dr. King believed that the LC was important for consciousness. He used to teach that its importance lies in linking the human mind to the spiritual world. King thoroughly studied ancient African science whilst he was alive. This led him to conclude that the LC was biological evidence to support the ancient African concept of the Black Dot being the doorway to the collective unconscious.

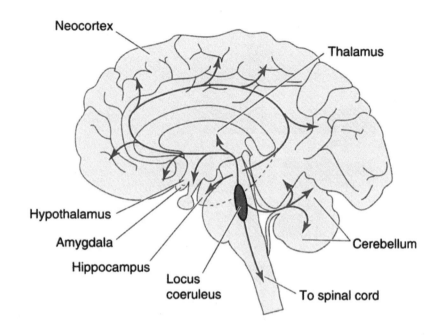

*Figure 9 - **Locus Coerleus***

Ok, so let's see how much you absorbed from this chapter. We went over the different types of melanin found in humans and it got quite deep there, I know. Don't worry though, this is why we end each chapter with a quiz to test your learning. Remember, the answers are located at the back of the book, but try not to look at the answers until after you've had a go at answering each question. Just like the first quiz, it's a multiple choice test and there's only one correct answer for each question. Good luck!

Melanin Quiz 2 – Different Types of Melanin

1 In humans, melanin exists in three forms
- **A.** Fleek, Poppin' and Drippin
- **B.** Negro-melanin, Caucaso-melanin, Monglo-melanin
- **C.** Eumelanin, Pheomelanin, Neuromelanin
- **D.** Chloromelanin, Allomelanin, Chlorophyll

2 Melanocytes are melanin-producing cells found in
- **A.** Skin and Hair Follicles
- **B.** Eyes and Inner Ears
- **C.** Bones, Heart and Brain
- **D.** All the above!

3 What are melanosomes?
- **A.** Tiny organelles inside melanocytes where melanin is synthesised and stored
- **B.** Tiny organelles outside melanocytes where melanin is synthesised and stored
- **C.** Large organelles inside water molecules where melanin is synthesised and stored
- **D.** Large organelles outside water molecules where melanin is synthesised and stored

4 The type of melanin your melanocytes produce depends on...
- **A.** The time of day
- **B.** Your genes
- **C.** The pH inside your melanosomes
- **D.** B & C

5 Eumelanin and Pheomelanin are synthesised within melanosomes of melanocytes by a series of chemical reactions starting with the amino acid...
- **A.** Tyrosine
- **B.** Lysine
- **C.** Histidine
- **D.** Cysteine

6 Neuromelanin, the type found in 12 centres in the brain, affects the way you...
- A. Move, Learn and Memorise
- B. See and Smell
- C. Hear and Taste
- D. All the above!

7 What substance in the brain plays an important role in the regulation of smooth coordinated movements?
- A. Locus Coeruleus
- B. Substantia Nigra
- C. Hypothalamus
- D. Meninges

8 What substance in the brain did Dr. Richard King call the Black Dot?
- A. Locus Coeruleus
- B. Substantia Nigra
- C. Hypothalamus
- D. Meninges

CHAPTER THREE

EMBRYOGENESIS

EMBRYOGENESIS

"The wonder of human reproduction begins with the uniting of two specialized sex cells called the sperm and the egg. Sperm cells and egg cells are called gametes when they are separated. However, the term zygote is used when they are united to form the human organism (embryo). From the earliest stages of human development, melanin is found in several critical sites in the embryo. –Dr. T. Owens Moore, Ph.D. (1995)"

In order to fully appreciate how important melanin is to human life it makes sense to explain its involvement in the first eight weeks of human growth and development. Embryogenesis is a complex process that occurs during the first eight weeks after fertilisation. This is where the embryo is formed and developed. At the beginning of the ninth week the embryo is termed a foetus. Before this foetus becomes a tiny human inside of the mother's womb it has to go through a series of biological stages. All of these stages require melanin to be present. In the book *Why Darkness Matters*, Dr. T. Owens Moore says that melanin and neuromelanin are part of the sensory-motor network from the earliest stages of embryogenesis [32].

"...the brain and the spinal cord are formed from the neural tube, the sensory-motor network extends from the neural crest and melanocytes in the skin come from the epidermal layer. Each site is dependent on the presence of melanin for proper physiological functioning."

Dr. Karl Maret, in his video lecture presentation from 2013 entitled *The Science Behind Chaga* said that melanin "is actually a very important molecule in any woman who's having a baby, because the foetus has all this melanin in it." He goes onto show a picture of a developing foetus 35 days into pregnancy and tells the audience to look at the eye. "Notice that the eye is pure melanin" he says, before dramatically pausing to indicate that something profound has just been said. There's a moment of silence in the room; and then in the background (if you have good hearing) you can hear an audience member say "Wow!" Dr. Karl Maret then continues, "That's an amazing picture isn't it? To see all this melanin is inside, and when the embryo first forms there is what's called the dark streak. That's all melanin!" The dark streak he is referring to is scientifically known as the primitive streak. It plays a crucial role in embryogenesis as it marks the start of gastrulation.

Gastrulation

Gastrulation has been described as the "black box" of human development by embryologist Lewis Wolpert. In an article published in 2016 by The Guardian entitled: *Inside the 'Black Box' of Human Development*, Lewis Wolpert is quoted as saying, "It is not birth, marriage or death, but gastrulation that is truly the most important time in your life" [33]. The article goes onto say that Human Gastrulation is the most momentous of all embryonic transformations. This is a very profound statement to make, and if you were to research what happens during gastrulation you may start to agree.

HUMAN EMBRYONIC DEVELOPMENT

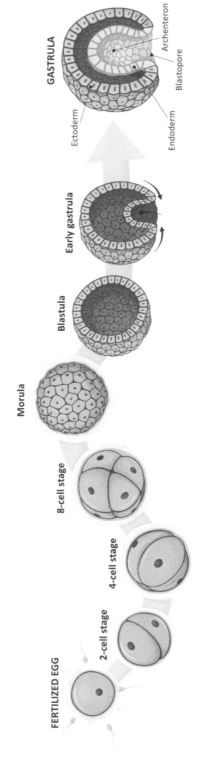

Figure 10 - Fertilization to gastrula

42

Gastrulation is defined as the early stage of embryonic development when the embryo transforms from a one-dimensional layer of epithelial cells (blastula) and reorganises into a multi-layered and multidimensional structure called the gastrula. What makes the gastrula so important? Why would one of the top embryologists say that gastrulation is "truly the most important time in your life"? Knowing what the gastrula does will help you understand this profound statement. The gastrula is trilaminar ("three-layered"). These three germ layers are known as the ectoderm (outer layer), mesoderm (middle layer) and endoderm (inner layer). Now I know we're getting very *"scientific"* right now and people start to doze off when they hear scientific terms, but try not to get lost here, this stuff is simple! The term "derm" means what? Even if you're not into science I'm sure you'll remember what this term means from school. It means skin. So during gastrulation the embryo develops into three layers of skin. These three layers of skin develop into all your bodily systems (nervous system, respiratory system, skeletal system etc.) and your organs. Yes, you read that right. Every organ in your body developed from three layers of <u>skin</u>.

Ectoderm gives rise to the epidermis (outer skin), sweat glands, hair, nails, lining of mouth and anus, cornea and lens of eye. The endoderm develops into the epithelium of the digestive system, endocrine and respiratory system, and organs associated with the digestive system such as the liver and pancreas. The mesoderm develops into many cell types, including muscle, bone, kidneys, connective tissue, reproductive and excretory system. Hopefully now you get why Lewis Wolpert said what he said. Everything you see when you look at yourself in the mirror was developed from three layers of SKIN. So, the next time someone says to you that skin is not important be sure to tell them about this book.

Following gastrulation, the next major development in the embryo is neurulation, which occurs during weeks three and four after fertilisation. This is a process in

GERM LAYERS

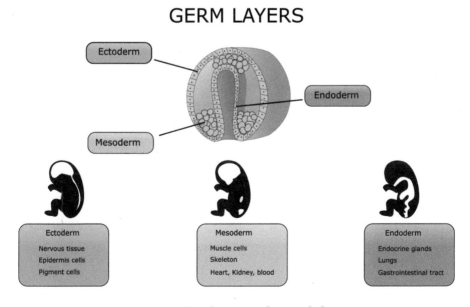

Figure 11 - **Ectoderm mesoderm endoderm**

43

which the ectoderm layer develops structures, including the neural crest that will eventually become your melanocytes and the nervous system. Melanocytes are multidendritic cells derived from the neural crest that look very similar to the structure of nerve cells in the brain. Neurons in the brain and melanocytes in the skin have the same embryological origin [Dr. T. Owens Moore, Ph.D].

Whilst gastrulation is happening on the inside of the pregnant woman's womb, triggered by the formation of a dark 'primitive streak', there is actually a melanin streak developing on the outside as well! Check out this excerpt from master teacher Dr. Llaila O. Afrika. This is taken from his book entitled: *The Power and Science of Melanin.*

> *"Melanin is increased (built) on the abdomen (so-called belly) of some pregnant women causing a dark line (linea nigra). Usually during the second trimester (3 months) of pregnancy the linea nigra dark line (melanin) begins above the center of the genital pubic hair and extends up to the breastbone of the chest. During pregnancy melanin darkens the nipples, genitals, and causes moles to darken. Sometimes before the linea nigra appears a pale line (linea alba) is form, which turns dark. The linea nigra melanin helps to make a protective barrier against the effects of ultraviolet sunrays. The biochemical melanin absorbs sunlight, and resists abrasions (damage) to cells."*

Embryogenesis Summary

- Melanin plays a crucial role (emphasis on crucial) in human embryogenesis
- One of the earliest stages of human embryonic development is the formation of a primitive streak
- This "dark" primitive streak is melanin and signals the beginning of gastrulation
- Whilst gastrulation occurs inside the womb another dark line of melanin called linea nigra is formed on the abdomen of the pregnant woman
- According to embryologist Lewis Wolpert gastrulation is "truly the most important time in your life"
- Gastrulation is when three types of skin (derm) develop into all the major body parts
- After gastrulation is neurulation, which is when the neural crest develops into melanocytes and nervous system
- Melanocytes determine the type of melanin produced throughout the body
- Development of a baby's nervous system depends on neuromelanin
- The nervous system determines the optimal functioning of all five senses
- Without the nervous system the baby wouldn't be able to see, feel, taste, smell or hear anything!
- These senses all depend on melanin

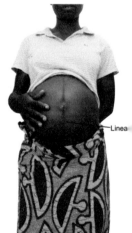

Linea

Figure 12
Linea Nigra

Embryonic Development

1ST TRIMESTER
- 1 MONTH
- 2 MONTH
- 3 MONTH

2ND TRIMESTER
- 4 MONTH
- 5 MONTH
- 6 MONTH

3RD TRIMESTER
- 7 MONTH
- 8 MONTH
- 9 MONTH

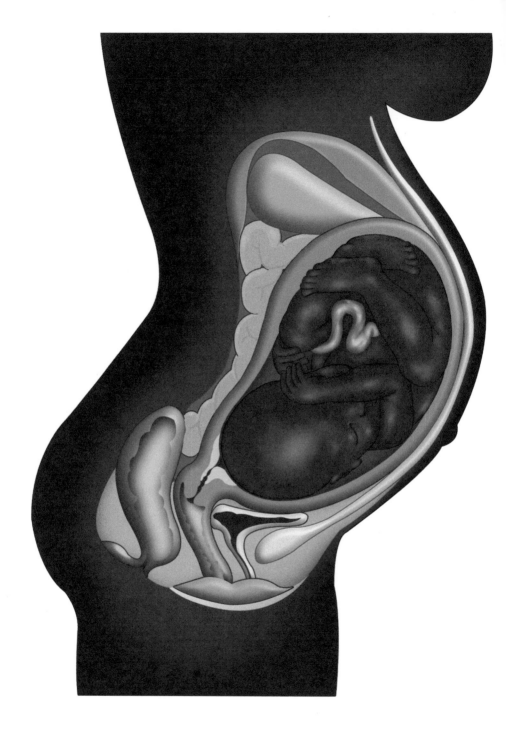

Figure 14
All Stages of Pregnancy Depend on Melanin

46

Melanin Quiz 3 – Embyogenesis

1 Embryogenesis is the complex process which occurs
    A.   during the first eight weeks after giving birth
    B.   during the first eight weeks after Valentine's Day
    C.   during the first eight weeks after fertilisation
    D.   during the first eight weeks after taking the morning-after pill

2 Gastrulation is one of the earliest stages of embryogenesis when the embryo develops into three layers of...
    A.   BLOOD *(heme)* – Ectoheme, Mesoheme, Endoheme
    B.   SKIN *(derm)* – Ectoderm, Mesoderm, Endoderm
    C.   BONE *(osteo)* – Ecto-osteo, Meso-osteo, Endo-osteo
    D.   SUGAR *(sacchar)* – Ectosaccaride, Mesosaccharide, Endosaccharide

3 The Ectoderm layer develops into
    A.   Outer Skin, Sweat Glands, Hair and Nails
    B.   Lining of Mouth and Anus
    C.   Neural Crest, Melanocytes and Nervous System
    D.   All the above!

4 The Endoderm layer develops into
    A.   The Digestive System
    B.   The Endocrine System
    C.   The Respiratory System
    D.   All the above!

5 The Mesoderm layer develops into
    A.   Muscle, Bone and Connective Tissues
    B.   Kidneys and Reproductive System
    C.   Excretory System
    D.   All the above!

6 What marks the start of gastrulation?
    A.   The Primitive Streak
    B.   Morning Sickness
    C.   Hunger Pangs
    D.   Period Pains

7 What is the name of the dark (melanin) line that appears on the abdomen of some women during pregnancy?
    A.   Linea Nigra
    B.   Linea Tigra
    C.   Linea Alba
    D.   Linea Alpha

CHAPTER FOUR
THE IMPORTANCE OF PIGMENTS

THE IMPORTANCE OF PIGMENTS

At this point in the book I'm sure you're starting to acknowledge the true importance of this pigment they call melanin to all human life on Earth. And rightly so, as it determines the quality of your brain and nervous system, skin, hair, eyes, ears, heart, and bones. It also determines how the embryo develops during embryogenesis. It seems the master teacher Dr. Llaila Afrika was right when he called this pigment the "chemical key to life." But it's not just the melanin pigment that is important to life as we know it. Once you start to delve deep into the encrypted scientific language the science community uses (especially in biology and chemistry) you'll find that the body is full of many pigments that help it to function optimally. Here are a few examples:

Photopigments / Visual Pigments

These are important pigments found in the eye that function in light reception by transforming light energy into electrical (nerve) signals. They consist of the following pigments:

Scotopsin – associated with vision in dim light
Rhodopsin – enables vision in low-light conditions
Melanopsin – known to mediate regulation of the circadian rhythms
Zeaxanthin and Lutein – yellow pigments found in the macula that protect the eye from light damage and oxidative stress. A loss of these pigments in the macula results in macular degeneration.

Without these pigments in the eye we wouldn't be able to see. We owe all of our vision, whether it's 20/20 or blurry, to these photopigments. Some of these pigments are available in nature and can be used to regenerate eye health. For example, Zeaxanthin and Lutein, which can be found in red, orange and yellow fruits, have been shown to improve retinal health and preserve vision. It is interesting to note that Lutein, which is an orange pigment found in the eye, requires orange fruits and vegetables to be topped up. Zeaxanthin, which is a yellow-coloured pigment, requires yellow fruits and vegetables to work optimally in the eye and Meso-zeaxanthin (another carotenoid found in the macular of the eye), which is red in colour, requires red fruits and vegetables. The relationship between the colour of plants and the colour of these photopigments should not be ignored. I'm sure you can see why. If you were to do some research on Zeaxanthin and Lutein you may find studies that suggest these two pigments do not just improve retinal health, but significantly improve brain function as well. This is due to enhanced brain blood flow and neural efficiency. As a golden rule, anything that is good for the eyes will be good for the brain as the eyes are directly connected to the brain.

Melanopsin

Another photopigment I suggest you research is Melanopsin. Melanopsin is the pigment that is involved in photoentrainment. In layman's terms this just means it trains the eye to know when it's day or night time, which keeps our biological clock ticking on time. Every living organism operates on a cycle, an internal clock. The human operates on the sleep/wake cycle which is commonly known as the circadian rhythm. Without melanopsin you wouldn't be able to keep to that cycle. It regulates our circadian rhythm by telling us when it's time to sleep or be alert. This bodily rhythm depends on the release of two important hormones from the pineal gland in the brain: Serotonin and Melatonin. Serotonin is the hormone released during the day and it's responsible for your alertness. At night, serotonin is converted into the hormone responsible for sleepiness, which is called Melatonin. This powerful hormone regulates the release of other hormones; including a family of melanin-dependant hormones called Melanocyte Stimulating Hormones or MSH (these are sometimes called melanocortins or melanotropins). The main MSH involved in melanogenesis is called alpha-Melanocyte Stimulating Hormone or α-MSH. As the name suggests, α-MSH stimulates the melanocytes to release melanin. This process cannot happen without melatonin. When I teach students about their circadian hormones I tell them that melatonin makes you feel mellow. After they hear that they never forget which is which out of serotonin and melatonin. How does this relate to melanopsin? Well, Melanopsin mediates our circadian rhythm by regulating the synthesis of melatonin. It does this through controlling the amount of light our eyes receive by expanding and narrowing the size of the pupil (pupillary light reflex).

Melanopsin is the most sensitive photopigment to the blue light spectrum. This just means blue light affects it the most. Where do we get most of our blue light exposure from in this technology driven society? Smartphones, laptops, tablets, and computer screens. An overload of blue light exposure could have a negative effect on melanopsin leading to sleep/wake cycle problems. This is why being on these devices before bed can directly affect your quality of sleep. Our eyes detect light regardless of whether they are open or closed. So sleeping with these devices on in your bedroom could still have an effect on your circadian rhythm, even though you're not on the device. Keep this in mind next time you decide to fall asleep whilst watching something on your smartphone or laptop.

Rhodopsin

Light detection is the most primary role your eyes play, and in order for your eyes to detect any light they need rhodopsin, which is found at the back of the eye, in the retina. The retina is the area of the eye that senses light, interprets that information, and transmits it to the brain for further interpretation. Now you might be thinking, "This is great info Leon, but what has this got to do with melanin?" Well, here's something that might just blow your mind. In a study published in 2011, biologists from Brown University reported that melanocyte skin cells detect ultraviolet light using a photosensitive receptor previously thought to exist only in the eye [34]. This eye-like ability of skin to sense light triggers the production of melanin within hours, more quickly than previously thought. The photosensitive receptor that they found inside melanocytes was rhodopsin. Yes, the same photopigment that detects light in your eyes is, in fact, inside of your melanin as well. Your skin can literally see! I'm just going to wait for that to sink in. Ridiculous as this may sound, it might not be that far-fetched when you think about it from your own experience. Have you ever wondered how you're capable of knowing that someone is looking at you without you looking at them? Has this ever happened to you? You're walking down a street and somehow you know that someone is staring at you. So you instinctively turn your head towards them, and to no surprise of yours they are staring right at you. Did your skin inform you of this? How did you know where to turn or who was looking at you? Was it your skin or your eyes that made you react to the feeling of being watched?

Studies have shown that melanin in the iris of the eye is directly related to an individual's reaction time or quickness of movement [35]. The darker the iris the better one was able to respond to external stimuli. Think about how that would translate to sports and athletics. In any athletic endeavour, being able to react to external stimuli and respond accordingly would be, in large parts, due to the melanin and rhodopsin in the eye. And you now know that rhodopsin is in the skin as well. Essentially this means you can see with your whole body, not just your eyes. Furthermore, there are studies to suggest that you can hear with your whole body too. According to a review article published by Archives in Neurology & Neuroscience (ANN), Dr. Alireza Bina found that sound might be transferred from our skin and eyes to the inner ear, indicating that the external auditory canal is not the only input of sound [36]. There is a part of the inner ear called the cochlea, a spiral-shaped bone that plays a key role in the sense of hearing. According to the ANN article, the cochlea receives sound from two separate directions: Forward Auditory Input pathway, which are the sound signals that come through directly from the external ear canal; and Backward Auditory Input pathways, which are the signals transferred from the skin and eyes to the cochlea. The cochlea receives sound from both directions and organizes and transfers them to the brain for ultimate processing [37].

So let's be clear: both your eyes and your skin are capable of seeing light and hearing sound. According to who? Leon Marshall? No! According to science. Matter of fact, there's been published scientific studies to suggest that your skin can smell too! Researchers at Bochum's Department for Cell Physiology in Germany reported that melanocytes have an olfactory receptor that allows the pigment-producing cell to smell scents [38]. Your melanin can see light, hear sounds and smell scents. And to think, there are some people who still downplay the importance of this pigment.

Plant Pigments

Many studies have shown that the body requires certain plant and algae pigments to function optimally. What's very interesting about these pigments is they all tend to be associated with antioxidants. Here are a few examples:

Plant Pigment	Common Types	Found in
Chlorophylls	Chlorophyll a, Chlorophyll b	Green Plants
Carotenoids	Carotenes and Xanthophylls	Yellow, Orange and Red Plants
Flavonoids	Flavanols and Anthocyanins	Blue, Purple and Red Plants
Betalains	Betacyanins and Betaxanthins	Red and Yellow Plants

Not only are all these plant pigments associated with antioxidants, studies show that the darker the fruit or vegetable is, the higher the antioxidant capacity. In a research paper entitled *Relationship between color and antioxidant capacity of fruits and vegetables* the researchers found that colour was related to antioxidant capacity in some plants, and that anthocyanin-rich foods were reported as having the highest capacity [39]. What foods are high in anthocyanins? Blackcurrants, blackberries,

51

blueberries, black beans, black grapes, and aubergine; just to name a few. These dark coloured fruits and vegetables seem to be very powerful antioxidants and studies have shown that it's actually the skin of these foods that carries the high antioxidant capacity. Notice that these foods tend to come from the Flavonoid family of plant pigments (look at the table of plant pigments). Flavonoids, which are the main type of polyphenols found in plants, are believed to help prevent or delay skin cell damage and other types of damage by counteracting oxidative stress from unstable molecules called free radicals [Liu-Smith, L Meyskens, 2016]. Polyphenols are plant compounds that offer various health benefits. Regularly consuming polyphenols is thought to boost digestion and brain health, as well as protect against heart disease, type 2 diabetes, and even certain cancers [40]. Over 4000 of 8000 known polyphenols are classified as flavonoids. These flavonoids exhibit melanogenic effects [41], meaning that they aid in the production of melanin due to their positive effect on the enzyme tyrosinase. Flavonoids also exhibit an anti-melanoma effect via inhibiting cancer cell proliferation and inducing apoptosis [41]. So there's likely to be a twofold benefit in consuming foods high in flavonoids:

(i) The Melanogenic Effect
(ii) The Anti-Melanoma Effect

One more time for emphasis: it is the skin of flavonoid foods, like the skin of dark-coloured berries, that carry these effects. The darker the berry, the better! For some reason, a Tupac lyric just came to mind.

Heme Pigments

The scientific definition of a 'pigment' is an organic compound that gives a characteristic colour to animal or plant tissue; and is involved in vital processes. That last part is very important to note. Pigments don't just determine the colour of living organisms; they are vital to how the living organism processes information. We are all aware of how vital chlorophyll is to the process of photosynthesis. Without it plants would not be able to convert light energy into chemical energy. You now know that melanin is vital to how your brain and nervous system process information. Without it your eyes for example, wouldn't be able to convert light energy into electrical signals. It makes you wonder why children are not taught about pigments in school, considering the key role they play in everyone's biology. I remember in science classes back when I was a child being taught about all the systems of the body. I was taught about the skeletal system, muscular system, cardiovascular system, endocrine system, digestive system and nervous system. I was never taught about the pigment system. We all have a pigment system, which is a system of pigments that carry out vital roles in our body. It's just the science community doesn't call it that. Instead, they use words like cytochrome or chromocyte to confuse you, hoping that you don't put two and two together and realise they are talking about pigments. For example, what is a cytochrome?

Cytochromes are electron transfer proteins that contain heme. What is heme? Heme are pigments. They are respiratory pigments containing iron that help carry oxygen around the body. Hence, wherever you find heme pigments present you'll also find oxygen transfer capabilities. Most people are aware of hemoglobin, the protein molecule in red blood cells that carry oxygen from the lungs to the body's tissues. But there are other respiratory pigments inside the human body that you should also be aware of, like myoglobin (the main oxygen-carrying pigment of muscle tissues). These heme pigments are essential to cellular respiration. Without heme pigments we wouldn't be able to breathe... literally! Here's an excerpt from a very old research paper entitled *HEMOGLOBIN, THE HEME PIGMENTS AND CELLULAR RESPIRATION* by M. L Anson and A.E Mirsky (1930) [42].

"Hemoglobin has long been studied as a carrier of oxygen in the blood of vertebrates. More recently (1885) a pigment related to hemoglobin was observed by MacMunn in the cells of a great variety of lower animals which have no hemoglobin either in their cells or their body fluids. After long neglect, MacMunn's observations were recalled, and were confirmed and extended. In addition still another pigment was discovered which is related to hemoglobin and which in cells acts as a respiratory catalyst. A group of pigments called heme pigments and closely related to hemoglobin is accordingly now known. They exist in all aerobic cells where one of them, at least, plays an essential role in cellular oxidation."

Many believe that the scientist who recalled, confirmed and extended the work of MacMunn was a scientist by the name of David Keilin. The story goes that Keilin decided to give these respiratory pigments a new name, so he called them cytochromes or "cellular pigments" and classified them as heme proteins. So from now on, anytime you see the word cytochrome used in biology or chemistry, understand what they're referring to: CELLULAR PIGMENTS. Why on Earth don't they just say that?! To be fair though, I don't blame the scientists who know this stuff but continue to use scientific jargon and words that the layman can't understand. The truth is right there staring you in the face. All you need to do is grab that super powerful fun-sized computer that's in your pocket (some people call them "smart" phones) and type these words into your search engine to see what they mean. That's what I do all the time. Anytime I hear a scientist use a term I'm not familiar with I grab my mini-computer and start doing some research on it. For example, if you did some research on the customarily used scientific term cytochrome you'd find that it's made up of the suffix CHROME which means "colour", and the prefix CYTO- which means "of a cell or cells." Therefore, CYTO-CHROME refers to the colour of a cell or cells. What gives cells and tissues their colour? PIGMENTS! Many of these words that the science community use, even though confusing at times, are quite easy to decode; because they tend to have the same root word. Just look at how many times the root word chrome is used in biology. You have chromosomes, chromatids, chromocytes, chromoblasts, chromaffins, chromophores, chromataphores; the list goes on and on. All of these biological terms have chrome as the root word which means they have something to do with colour (pigments). This makes the study of pigments arguably the most important thing to study in biology.

Pigments in Biology

CHROMOSOME: a long DNA molecule with part or all of the genetic material of an organism

CHROMATID: one half of a duplicated chromosome. Before replication, one chromosome is composed of one DNA molecule. In replication, the DNA molecule is copied, and the two molecules are known as chromatids

CHROMOCYTE: a pigmented anatomical cell

CHROMOBLAST: an embryonic cell that develops into a pigment cell

CHROMAFFIN: a type of cell that makes neurohormones (chemicals that are made by nerve cells and used to send signals to other cells) and releases them into the blood. Chromaffin cells make epinephrine (adrenaline) and norepinephrine (noradrenaline)

CHROMOPHORE: the part of a molecule that absorbs light at a specific frequency and so imparts colour to the molecule

CHROMATAPHORES: are cells that produce colour (pigment-bearing cells of lower vertebrates and invertebrates)

Human blood
Hemoglobin

Plant
Chlorophyll

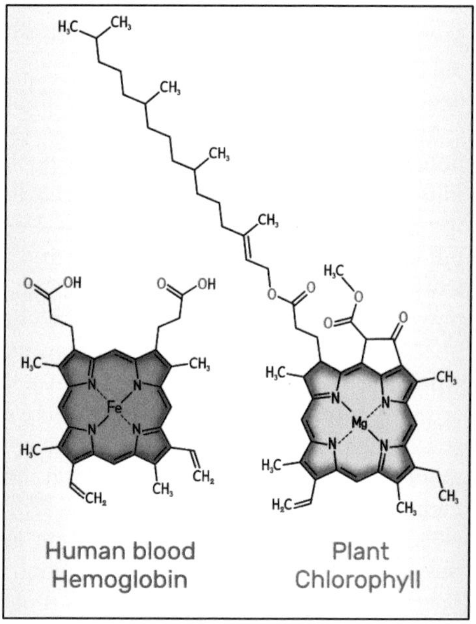

Figure 15
Notice the similarities between the heme pigment in red blood cells (hemoglobin) and the plant pigment in plant cells (chlorophyll)

There's literally no way to study biology without studying pigments. And the same goes for chemistry. Therefore, in order to understand the biochemistry of human beings you must study pigments. If you wanted to study your own biochemistry for example, your blood would need to be analysed. The effectiveness of the heme pigment in your blood determines how much oxygen it carries. Every cell in your body relies on this oxygen carrying heme pigment. This is just one of many examples of how essential pigments are to your biology. You are full of pigments! And these pigments inside of you are of the utmost importance because of one main reason: They absorb light frequencies. Your melanin can then convert these light energies into a different type of usable energy needed for cellular processes. What's interesting to note about pigments is the distinct colour of their appearance, which is actually due to the light frequencies that they are not absorbing. So for example, chlorophylls are green because they absorb all of the visible light frequencies of the sun except green. They actually reflect green to your eye and that's why they appear green. Blueberries are blue because they reflect blue and absorb all the other visible light frequencies of the sun. Yellow bananas are yellow because that's the light frequency they are reflecting back to your eye. The yellow banana is

Absorption and reflection of light

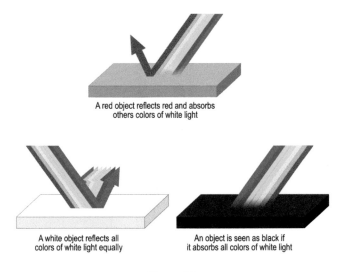

A red object reflects red and absorbs
others colors of white light

A white object reflects all
colors of white light equally

An object is seen as black if
it absorbs all colors of white light

Figure 16
Light Absorption and Reflection

not absorbing yellow light frequencies. I hope this makes sense. The colour of a pigment is the colour it's reflecting, not absorbing.

To fully appreciate what pigments are absorbing and reflecting it might help to have a visual image of the electromagnetic spectrum in your mind. I know from being a university lecturer that we all have different learning styles. For example, some of us have an auditory learning style. Auditory learning means that a student learns most effectively by listening. A kinaesthetic learner is someone who needs to be actively engaged in their learning. They are 'tactile' learners who use movement, testing, trial and error and a non-traditional learning environment to retain and recall information. Then there's the visual learner. The visual learner needs to see information in order to process it. They understand and remember things by sight. They can process mental images of what they are learning and learn best by using methods that are primarily visual. Examples of this include utilising graphs, charts, maps, diagrams, and other forms of visual stimulation to effectively interpret information. I've been a university lecturer for over 15 years now and through my many observations of students in classrooms I can honestly say that every single one of them uses all three of these learning styles when they are presented with new information. However, we all have a preference, a style that we naturally utilise more than the others. That style for many of us is the visual learning style, hence the reason why throughout this book I have included images and diagrams to help explain the science you are learning.

Electromagnetic Spectrum

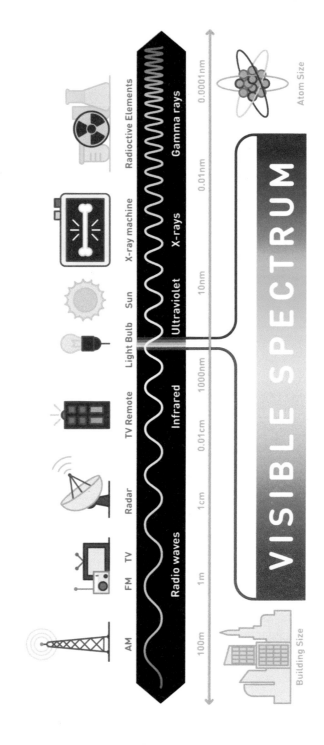

Figure 17
Electromagnetic spectrum

The Electromagnetic Spectrum

With that being said, look at Figure 16 and see if this helps you understand the relationship between pigments and light. It's very simple, pigments absorb light. But what type of light will the pigment absorb? Here's where a visual of the electromagnetic spectrum may help (see Figure 17). What is the electromagnetic spectrum? It is the term used by scientists to describe the entire range of light that exists in the known universe. Light has been described as a wave of alternating electric and magnetic fields from radio waves to gamma rays. When most people think of light, they think of the light that they can see. But most of the light in the universe is, in fact, invisible to us. There is only a tiny fraction of the whole spectrum that our eyes detect as light, and that's the visible spectrum. The sun emits the visible spectrum as white light. If you were to look directly at the sun (not advised for people with sensitive eyes) you'd see white light. In 1672, the famous scientist Sir Isaac Newton demonstrated that the clear white light emitted from the sun was actually composed of seven visible colours. He was able to show this by refracting sunlight through a prism (see Figure 18).

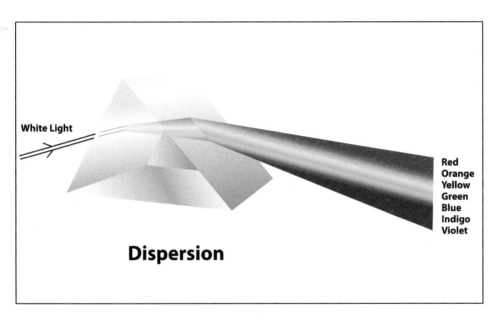

Figure 18
Light Through Prism

He observed the way white light would separate and appear to bend as it passed through the prism creating all the colours we see in a rainbow. This was revolutionary at the time as it helped scientists understand the visible part of the electromagnetic spectrum. Light from the sun comes in three main forms: Ultraviolet, Infrared, and Visible. Pigments play an important role in absorbing all three, especially the seven different colours of the visible spectrum.

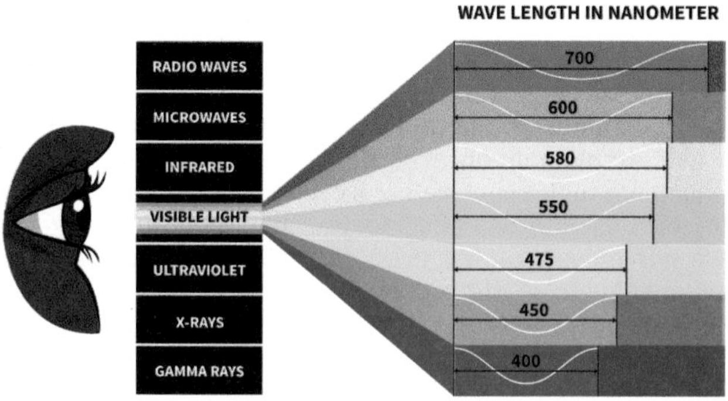

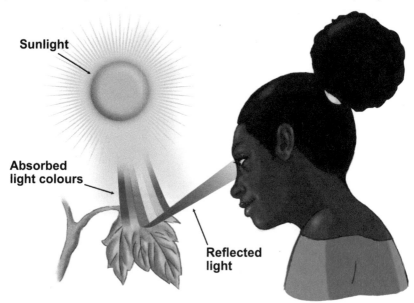

Figure 19
How The Naked Eye Sees Color

How We See Colour

The visible spectrum consists of 7 main colours that our naked eye can detect: Red, Orange, Yellow, Green, Blue, Indigo, Violet. You can remember the order of the colours in the visible spectrum with the mnemonic ROY-G-BIV. When a pigment absorbs parts of the visible spectrum it will reflect whatever colours it is not absorbing to your eyes. So for example, green leaves absorb ROY (red, orange and yellow) and BIV (blue, indigo and violet), but reflect G (green). Your eyes look at the leaves and see the colour it's reflecting (G), not the colours that have been absorbed (ROY BIV). Red apples absorb OY-G-BIV (orange, yellow, green, blue, indigo and violet) and reflect R (red). Blueberries absorb ROY-G-IV and reflect B (blue).

Figure 20a
How We See Green Leaves

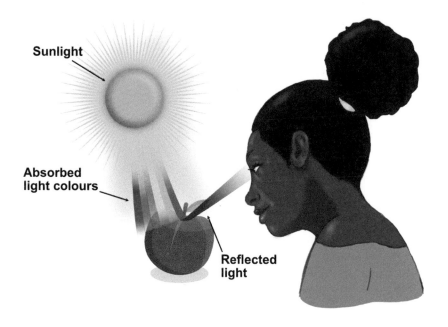

Figure 20b
How We See Red Apples

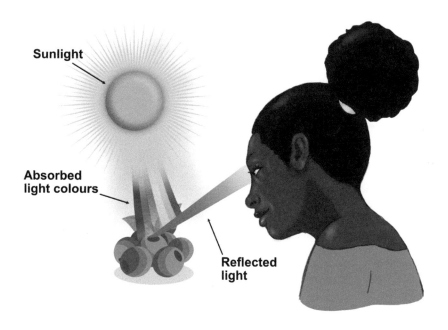

Figure 20c
How We See Blueberries

59

So, when you look at all the different colour fruits and vegetables that mother nature has provided for us, hopefully now you can appreciate that the wide variety of colours we see are due to pigments absorbing and reflecting light. This is very important to note, as I'm sure when you were young, you were encouraged to eat a rainbow of fruits and vegetables by your elders. In order for melanin to function optimally it needs a wide variety of nutrients which can be acquired through a colourful diet. Eating the ROY-G-BIV rainbow is a great way to ensure your melanin is getting all the vitamins and minerals it requires to do its job. This may seem quite obvious after you learn that the colours you see in nature represent the absorption of the visible spectrum. What may not seem so obvious is why melanin appears to be black in colour. What is it absorbing? And what is it reflecting to appear black? Melanin is black because it absorbs all the colours of the visible spectrum and reflects none. That means the colours ROY-G-BIV are all part of melanin, hence the reason why the colour of fruits and vegetables in your diet should be ROY-G-BIV. In other words, you should be consuming a rainbow diet. Many of us know this instinctively anyway. Even a child knows not to just consume one fruit all the time. Common sense and boredom would kick in at some point. Consuming just one type of fruit (or just one type of pigment) would inevitably lead to an imbalance of vitamins and minerals needed for optimal health. It's interesting to note however, that pheomelanin, the red and yellow type of melanin pigment, specifically needs red and yellow foods to improve its function. I always say science is simple, it's logic backed up by evidence. So, where is the evidence of this? Well, nowadays we all have smartphones, so it might be an idea to grab that smartphone and make your phone smart. Meaning, do some research on it and make it tell you something you didn't know. Here's a few examples of what you can type into your smart phone:

- How to increase melanin
- How to boost melanin production
- Ways to increase melanin in skin

Type these in verbatim or type in something similar into your preferred search engine and see what results pop up. You'll notice that nearly all the websites that describe how to top up melanin suggest the same thing: Vitamin A. Most of the sites you visit will say you need antioxidant Vitamins A, C and E, as these are all powerful antioxidants that can help with both types of skin melanin [43]. But research has shown that the fat-soluble Vitamin A, more than any other, may be the key to healthy pheomelanin production [43]. Now what foods are high in Vitamin A? Carrots, Butternut Squash, Pink Grapefruit, Pumpkin, Tomatoes, Sweet Potatoes, Cantaloupe, Red Bell Peppers, Dried Apricots to name but a few. Notice how all of these foods are either red, orange or yellow in colour. Just think about that for two seconds, red and yellow foods increase the red and yellow type of melanin. You see how science is simple? These are all plant sources of Vitamin A, but there are animal sources too. Vitamin A can be found in high amounts in beef liver, lamb liver, mackerel, salmon, tuna, cheese, cow's milk, butter and eggs. These types of foods may be beneficial for someone who is pheomelanin dominant. Why? Because Vitamin A increases pheomelanin. Hopefully you can put two and two together as to why all of these websites would be promoting a diet specifically for pheomelanin-dominant individuals and not for eumelanin.

What would be the best diet for someone who is eumelanin dominant? What vitamin do they require more of? Vitamin D! The powerful antioxidant vitamins A, C and E are necessary as well, but the main vitamin needed for Eumelanin dominant individuals is Vitamin D. Hence the reason why if you have darker skin you need to be out in the sun longer for adequate Vitamin D synthesis [44-46]. A Vitamin D precursor is synthesised by the cholesterol in your skin when your melanin is exposed to UVB light. This Vitamin D precursor then goes through more synthesising in your liver and kidneys, before your kidneys produce the bioactive form of Vitamin D. This is the most reliable way for you to get more Vitamin D, by getting more sun! Any other way is unreliable, with varying results. With regards to foods, this too would be an unreliable way to get more Vitamin D as there are hardly any foods that contain this powerful vitamin. So, what foods should someone who is eumelanin-dominant consume? I go into detail about the specific foods to eat in a later chapter, but for now just remind yourself what colours from the visible spectrum black melanin can absorb. Can it absorb R? Can it absorb O? Y? G? B? I? V? The answer is all of them! Melanin can absorb all colours from the visible spectrum. So, your diet needs to consist of all colours (a wide variety of plant pigments). Now try this out as an experiment. Go to your local fruits and veg store and see what colours they have on offer. If you don't see the full ROY-G-BIV spectrum then you are missing out on key nutrients that could help top up your melanin. Most supermarkets here in the UK tend to have ROY-G covered in their fruit and veg section, but the darker coloured variety of BIV are not as readily available. For some reason they're not as abundant as the ROY-G colours or they're not as easy to find. But search for them as these fruits will undoubtedly have the higher antioxidant content that will keep your melanin sweet. Thank you, Mr. Shakur.

Melanin Quiz 4 – The Importance of Pigments

1 All pigments have a common role in biology, which is to...
- A. Absorb light
- B. Block light
- C. Absorb sugar
- D. Block sugar

2 What are photopigments?
- A. Pigs who like to take selfies
- B. Important pigments found in the eye that receive light and transform light energy into electrical (nerve) signals
- C. Important pigments found in the nose that receive odours and transform odours into aromas
- D. All the above

3 According to a University study published in 2011, which photopigment found in the eye is also found in the skin?
- A. Scotopsin
- B. Rhodopsin
- C. Melanopsin
- D. Zeathanthin

4 Research shows that the melanin in your skin has the ability to?
- A. See Light
- B. Hear Sounds
- C. Smell Scents
- D. All the above

5 Which pigments help green plants absorb light energy and convert it into chemical energy?
- A. Carotenoids
- B. Chlorophylls
- C. Betalains
- D. Flavanoids

6 Anthocyanin-rich foods are known to have the highest antioxidant capacity. What foods are high in anthocyanins?
- A. Blackcurrants, blackberries, black beans, black grapes
- B. Yellow bananas, yellow lemons, yellow apples
- C. White meat, white sugar, white rice, white milk
- D. Brown toast, brown burgers, brown tea

7 **What are Heme Pigments?**
  A. Plant pigments containing magnesium that help carry water around the body
  B. Visual pigments containing chromium that help carry chrome around the body
  C. Respiratory pigments containing iron that help carry oxygen around the body
  D. Skin pigments containing copper that help carry carbon around the body

8 **What are cytochromes?**
  A. Cellular pigments
  B. Respiratory pigments
  C. Heme pigments
  D. All the above

9 **A green leaf appears green because the chlorophyll pigment inside the leaf is?**
  A. Absorbing green
  B. Reflecting green
  C. Absorbing nothing
  D. Reflecting nothing

10 **What colours of the visible spectrum can eumelanin absorb?**
  A. Red, Orange and Yellow (ROY only)
  B. Blue, Indigo, Violet (BIV only)
  C. ALL (ROY-G-BIV)
  D. Green (G only)

CHAPTER FIVE
MELANOGENESIS

MELANOGENESIS

Melanogenesis is the complex process by which the pigment melanin is produced in melanosomes from melanocytes. As you now know from reading this book, it is the melanosomes inside of the melanocytes that produce either eumelanin or pheomelanin which determines the colour of our skin, hair and eyes. This is mainly dependent on genes and the pH inside of the melanosome. Pheomelanin naturally has more of an acidic pH due to the presence of cysteine (sulphur) in its molecular structure. This can be seen in Figure 21 which shows the melanin chemical pathway inside of the melanosome. As you can see, both eumelanin and pheomelanin production start off the same way: The amino acid Tyrosine gets converted into an amino acid compound called Dopa and then Dopa gets converted into Dopaquinone (an electron transporter). These first steps are made possible by the enzymatic activity of tyrosinase. Enzymes speed up chemical reactions in the body, and thus tyrosinase speeds up the production of melanin. After Dopa gets converted to Dopaquinone, the melanin chemical pathways split and follow different steps depending on the presence of sulphur (Cysteine) in the genetic makeup of the individual.

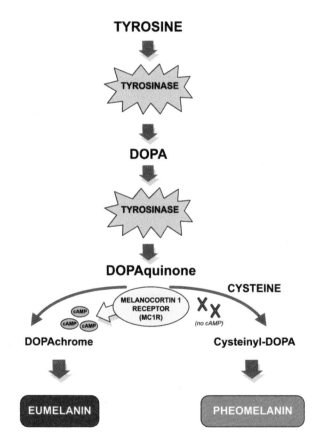

Figure 21
Melanin chemical pathway

Regardless of what type of melanin is produced by the melanosome, the process of melanogenesis happens within all of us on a daily basis. It is a must for this process to happen daily due to the important role this pigment plays in biological processes within the human body. The fact that melanocytes are located all over the body should indicate to you its importance to your biology. As nearly every scientist has proven over the many years of research on this topic, melanin is not just found in the skin of human beings. It is found in organs, the heart, the eyes, ears, blood and brain. Decades ago, it was believed that melanin was originally produced by the pineal gland in the brain. The pineal gland became the focal point for many discussions and lectures around melanin and to this day many still believe that the pineal gland is the focal point of melanogenesis. Melanin is produced all over the body, so there is not one focal point of production. However, your pineal gland does play a primary role in the process of melanogenesis, and this may be the reason why the 'third eye' has been emphasised so much by melanin scholars in the past.

Pineal Gland

The pineal gland, sometimes called the third eye or the mind's eye, is one of the most fascinating nervous system organs in the human body. Hidden deep in the midline of the two cerebral hemispheres, this small pea-shaped gland secretes melatonin or the hormone of darkness. During the night this influential hormone gets released into the blood and helps to regulate sleep and wakefulness and the circadian patterns that have broad effects on our health. The pineal gland receives many neural connections from the autonomic nervous system and it gets feedback control from suprachiasmatic nucleus (SCN) which receives retinal optic impulses to maintain circadian rhythm. The main function of the pineal gland is to receive information about the state of the light-dark cycle from the environment and convey this information to produce and secrete melatonin. The rhythmic production of melatonin keeps the internal circadian clock ticking on time. Melatonin is so vital to the sleep / wake rhythm of the individual that it is often used as a therapy for certain sleep disorders related to circadian rhythm abnormalities and for the alleviation of jet lag. It might have more extensive therapeutic applications in the future, since multiple physiological roles have been attributed to melatonin [47]. In addition to its role in regulating the circadian system and sleep patterns, melatonin is involved in cell protection, neuroprotection, and regulating the reproductive system, among other functions listed below. Melatonin is actually made from the conversion of serotonin, an influential daytime hormone that affects our mood and behaviour. The pineal gland is responsible for this conversion and as you will see, this conversion is crucial to the process of melanogenesis.

There are 5 main things that the pineal gland is responsible for:

1) Inner Eye – Sensing light and darkness
2) Biological Clock – Tell our bodies when to do its functions
3) Pacemaker – Sets the pace or rhythm for the body
4) Compass – Helps us orient ourselves
5) Secretory Organ – Secretes serotonin & melatonin

Additional Functions of Melatonin
• Regulate night and day cycles (sleep-wake cycles)
• Regulates mood, learning and memory
• Regulates immune activity
• Regulates dreaming
• Regulates fertility and reproduction
• Regulates hormone release, especially for reproduction and sexual maturation
• Slows down aging (antioxidant)
• Regulates melanogenesis [48]

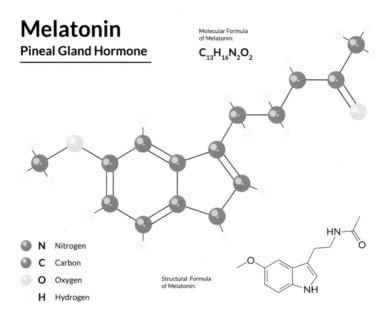

Melatonin
Pineal Gland Hormone

Molecular Formula
of Melatonin:

$C_{13}H_{16}N_2O_2$

N   Nitrogen
C   Carbon
O   Oxygen
H   Hydrogen

Structural Formula
of Melatonin:

*Figure 22 - **Melatonin Molecular structure***

Circadian Rhythm

Melanogenesis is triggered by intracellular and extracellular signals which all determine the quality and amount produced during the process. We must look at melanogenesis as an ongoing process and not just as this one thing that happens when we're out in the sun. It is a process that requires internal and external chemical reactions to take place in order for the process to continue. For example, a very important internal chemical reaction that must take place inside the body is the conversion of serotonin into melatonin. Serotonin is produced mainly in the gut during the day and then converted to melatonin at night, via the pineal gland. This is a very important step in the process as the release of melatonin at night activates the pituitary gland to secrete a family of melanin hormones called MSH (Melanocyte Stimulating Hormones), of which α-MSH (alpha-Melanocyte Stimulating Hormone) being the most important for melanin production. When α-MSH is released it stimulates the melanocytes to produce melanin. Melanosomes inside of the melanocytes fill up with melanin and then once they are full, they are transported along the dendrites of the melanocytes into the keratinocytes (the major cell type of the epidermis). See Figure 23 for a visual breakdown of what you just read.

If the pineal gland doesn't convert serotonin into melatonin the whole melanogenesis process is hindered. If not enough melatonin is present in the bloodstream at night or even if there's too much melatonin present in the bloodstream during the day, this can have an adverse effect on your circadian rhythm. According to melanin scholar Sistah Deborah Maat, what time you go to bed is an important factor in melatonin production. Twelve midnight seems to be the cut-off point. If you go to bed (and fall asleep) before twelve midnight you tend to produce more melatonin. If you get to bed after twelve midnight this drastically decreases the amount of melatonin in the bloodstream. It should come as no surprise then that night shift workers tend to have issues with their circadian rhythm. They are awake when they should be asleep and asleep when they should be awake. Anything that affects the biological rhythm of a living organism will no doubt affect the biological health of that living organism.

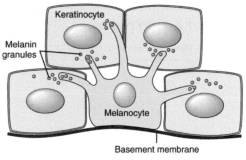

Figure 23
Melanocytes to keratinocytes

Rhythm and health go hand-in-hand in nature. There's no way a living organism can stay healthy if its natural rhythm is disturbed. This universal law goes for plants, trees, animals and humans. We all function optimally when we follow a natural rhythm based on the night and day cycle. If you don't believe me, speak to one of your friends or family members who have been doing night shift work for many years, and ask them about their health. You'll be surprised by how many health issues they suffer from. Science is simple. You can't cheat the laws of nature. All of nature follows a rhythm. That rhythm is directly linked to the sun cycle. This is why melatonin is so important to our health; its very nature is to keep us in harmonic rhythm with the universe.

Figure 24
Circadian rhythm

Melanogenesis Regulators

During the day ultraviolet radiation becomes the main regulator of melanogenesis in humans. UVA and UVB directly stimulate melanin production, leading to induced pigmentation of the skin (eumelanin), or 'tanning' (pheomelanin). Ultraviolet radiation increases proliferation and recruitment of melanocytes to the epidermis, as well as the production of melanosomes in both eumelanin-dominant and pheomelanin-dominant individuals. Studies show that there's an increase in reactive oxygen species when pheomelanin is exposed to UV rays during the day for too long. Reactive oxygen species are free radicals that can damage DNA. Hence, the reason why those with higher levels of pheomelanin tend to seek protection from the sun by using sunscreen.

During the night, the major internal regulator of melanogenesis is melatonin secreted from the pineal gland. This secretion aids in a good night's sleep, pituitary gland activation and cell repair. At night, when you are fast asleep, your body goes into repair mode and starts repairing any damage to cells, tissues and organs as a matter of priority. The DNA repair associated with melanin is done at night due to the enhancing effects of melatonin [49]. This means that a lack of melatonin, in other words a lack of sleep, will result in the body not fully repairing itself; causing cells, tissues and organs to become weakened over time. This is a very important mental note to make: If you want to heal, or repair, or recover from any cellular damage you must ensure you are getting enough sleep for the optimal regeneration of cells to occur.

Like the janitor who comes in at night to clean the floors and wash the windows, melatonin is the body's most powerful detoxification and rejuvenation agent. Every cell in your body benefits from melatonin's rejuvenation process. Melatonin acts like the road workers who do their job at night, building and repairing thousands of miles of road so that the cars are free to move around on them the next day. It is important that this job is done at night when the roads are less busy. Same with melatonin, it is important for this hormone to do its job at night when your metabolism is less busy. It's worth mentioning however, that studies show melatonin is actually produced first by the eye during the day and then ocular melatonin helps liberate melatonin in the pineal gland in response to the absence of light [50]. This is a very significant point to make, the fact that melatonin production relies on daytime sunlight through the eye should create a quantum leap in your consciousness. It is a point that I would like to emphasise.

Light and Melatonin

Sunlight through the eye starts the process of melanogenesis by activating ocular melatonin which helps with the conversion of serotonin to melatonin by the pineal gland at night. Although melatonin is known as the darkness hormone it is activated by light. This alone should show you the importance of receiving sunlight through your eyes every day to help keep your circadian rhythm (your internal biological clock) ticking on time. Anything that blocks sunlight going through your eyes will affect ocular melatonin and therefore melanogenesis. This includes sunglasses, eyeglasses, windows and contact lenses.

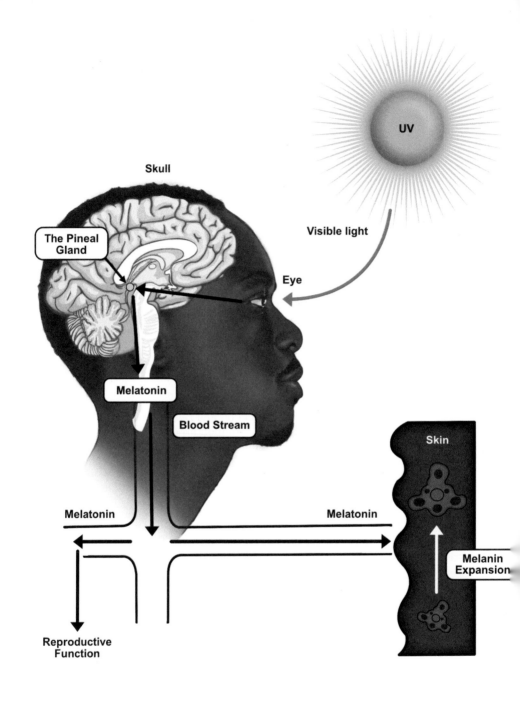

Figure 25
Melanogenesis through the eye

70

You don't have to sun gaze to receive light directly through the eye. All you need to do is allow your eyes to be exposed to natural outdoor light daily. This might be difficult for those who have very sensitive eyes to light. However, please keep in mind the process of melanogenesis always starts with sunlight through the eyes. This is not my opinion by the way, this is science. I can't tell you how many times I see eumelanin-dominant individuals outside in the sun with shades on. I'm sure they do it for fashion purposes; yes they do look cool. However, many of them have issues with direct sunlight through the eyes. Their eyes are so sensitive to the sun that they actually need to wear sunglasses. This could potentially be problematic in the long run, as wearing shades blocks the first step of melanogenesis. Again, this is not my opinion, this is science. And science is simple; it's just logic and evidence. Have you noticed how many people have issues with their eyes? How many people wear prescription glasses due to short-sightedness or myopia? I find it quite strange to see so many black and brown-eyed individuals with eye issues; especially considering the more eumelanin you have in your iris, the more light frequencies your eyes can absorb. Therefore, you should have the strongest eyesight, not the weakest. What's going on?

Eyesight and Melanogenesis

Why is everyone's eyesight deteriorating? Why are so many children wearing glasses these days? We've been conditioned to think that sunlight damages the eyes, when in fact, sunlight is nutrition for the eyes [51]. The first light that goes through your eyes upon awakening should really be sunlight. We need to look at sunlight as breakfast for our eyes. And like the old saying goes: "breakfast is the most important meal of the day." Allow your eyes to feed off of the nutrients that the sun provides every morning. Give your eyes what they need to start the melanogenic process inside of you. Light is synonymous with knowledge, hence the term 'enlightenment.' So open your eyes to the sun and become more enlightened. Natural sunlight is seen as a threat to our eye health in this smartphone era we find ourselves in. This is backwards logic. The first light that goes through most people's eyes upon awakening is the artificial blue light from their smartphone. This type of blue light inhibits ocular melatonin production leading to a disrupted melanogenesis process. Studies show that the blue light from electronic devices, including laptops and smartphones, can severely disrupt circadian rhythm, leading to poor sleeping habits. Anything that disrupts your circadian rhythm will disrupt melanogenesis as well. Imagine if your daily travel to work was disrupted. Imagine if every day there were major delays on your commute to work. How would this affect your day? How would getting to work late everyday affect your job? Apply this same logic to the melanogenesis process being disrupted or delayed. Due to the majority of us being miseducated or simply uneducated about melanin, very few of us are aware of how important our eyes are to the production of melanin. Light through our eyes initiates the process. However, the process continues after our eyes shut at night due to the important role of melatonin. Therefore, if our eyes are open when they should be closed this will slow the process down or cause a major disruption to it. The main culprit for keeping our eyes open at night is the blue light emitted from smartphones.

Blue Light Emission

As the popularity of smartphones continues to increase and the high frequency EMF's they emit get stronger, there's been growing concerns about the potential for blue light to harm eye tissue. What is it about blue light that makes it so dangerous to eye health? Recent studies suggest that blue light passes through the cornea and lens to the retina causing diseases such as dry eye, cataract and age-related macular degeneration. In addition to these findings blue light from smartphones has also been shown to inhibit melatonin secretion and enhance adrenocortical hormone production, which destroys the hormonal balance and directly affects sleep quality [52]. Keep in mind that the sun emits all the light frequencies of the visible spectrum (ROY-G-BIV), so during the day your eyes are exposed to all the colours of the rainbow, including blue light. However, exposure to just one light frequency instead of the full spectrum can become hazardous. It's like plants in nature; most are harmless to human health when consumed as a whole, but once you extract and isolate a particular substance, this isolated nutrient could be made into a harmless supplement or an addictive drug. Most of the common drugs used today are derived from plants. Case in point, cocaine is derived from coca leaves and the active ingredient in aspirin (salicin) is extracted from willow bark. Caffeine, although not considered a drug is itself very addictive, and is extracted from native kola-nuts, cocoa beans and of course coffee. All of these extractions, once isolated can become quite addictive on their own. As is the same with blue light; if received as part of the full visible spectrum of radiation emitted by the sun during the day it won't be as harmful to your eyes as the isolated and very concentrated artificial blue light your eyes receive constantly from your smartphone. The high energy, short wavelength of blue light activates feelings of alertness and cognitive function when our eyes are exposed to sunlight. These feelings are absolutely fine and necessary during daylight hours, but at night can become hazardous to eye health and sleep. Research suggests that many young people are addicted to using their phones before bedtime, exposing their sensitive eyes to perhaps the most dangerous light frequency available to them at home. Dozens of studies have investigated whether exposure to the artificial blue light emitted by smartphones over time could cause serious, long-term eye damage. And it's not just smartphones. There are many devices in your home that emit this high frequency light.

Common sources of blue light include:

- Laptops
- Fluorescent lights
- LED lights
- Smartphones
- Televisions
- Computer screens
- Tablets
- E-readers
- Video game consoles
- Any digital handheld device

Many people stay up late watching their favourite programmes online or on their smart TV's. Streaming services are capitalising on this with non-stop content for you to consume whilst your eyes stay open. With the use of social media and streaming services at an all-time high, what do you think will happen to the eye health of the next generation?

Social Media, Streaming Services and Sleep

There's no doubt that social media and streaming services have transformed the world we live in. Social media apps allow users to connect with people all over the globe in an instant, providing live interactions, news, and endless entertainment. Streaming services have seen a huge boost in subscriptions ever since the coronavirus pandemic began in 2020. In the UK, for example, a surge in screen time during lockdowns saw UK adults spend 40% of their waking day watching TV and online streaming services; according to media watchdog Ofcom [53]. At the height of the first lockdown in the UK, adults spent an average of six hours and 25 minutes each day staring at screens. People watched streaming services, such as Netflix, Amazon Prime Video and Disney+, with many becoming first-time subscribers. Ofcom found that viewing Figures for video streaming services were up 71% from the year before the pandemic, proving that the majority of us are now spending more time in front of screens than ever before. What is this doing to our eyesight? How will this affect our circadian rhythm? If we're being honest, many of us are guilty of taking our phones, tablets or laptops to bed and scrolling through social media newsfeeds or watching a movie on a streaming app before falling asleep. For lots of people, young and old, it's now the norm to sleep with a smartphone in the bedroom. Polls have shown that browsing social media is now one of the most common pre-sleep activities, between going to bed and falling sleep.

By reading this chapter I hope it's becoming clear how important sleep is to the melanogenesis process. Without adequate amounts of quality sleep each night your melatonin will struggle to repair cells (including DNA cells), your melatonin will struggle to activate the pituitary gland to release α-MSH and therefore α-MSH will struggle to stimulate the production of melanin from melanocytes. Hopefully it goes without saying what staying on social media apps and streaming services late into the night will do to your health. Especially when you consider that these companies intentionally want you to do that. It's no secret that social media companies and streaming services want you hooked on their content 24/7. One of Facebooks founding presidents, Sean Parker, once admitted that when Facebook was being developed the objective was: "How do we consume as much of your time and conscious attention as possible?" Parker, who has since left the company, was very vocal about the addictive properties of the social networking giant. "It literally changes your relationship with society, with each other. It probably interferes with productivity in weird ways. God only knows what it's doing to our children's brains," he said. So, the people behind these companies know exactly what they are doing and how it affects the consumers' circadian rhythm. Even the CEO of Netflix, Reed Hastings, once admitted that the streaming giants biggest rival is sleep. "You know, think about it, when you watch a show from Netflix and you get addicted to it, you stay up late at night. We're competing with sleep, on a margin" he said. So, these billion dollar companies are intentionally trying to figure out ways to disrupt your circadian rhythm, leading to a weakened melanin production process. Maybe after reading this people will start to realise that the sun is not our enemy. Many people want to wag their finger at the sun when it burns them due to weak melanin production, when in fact our disrupted circadian rhythm could be playing a major role. Once again for emphasis: Anything that disrupts your circadian rhythm will disrupt melanogenesis.

Melanogenesis Inhibition

It may help to look at melanogenesis as a night and day process, and not just a day process. Although our melanin is not directly increasing during the night, steps are being taken to ensure that the melanocytes release optimal amounts of melanin into keratinocytes (the outer most layer of skin) during the day. So many factors can disrupt this step-by-step process leading to weak melanin production. We've touched on sleep (or a lack thereof) being a major factor. But another one of the main factors is sugar. Having high blood sugar levels can actually inhibit the activity of tyrosinase. Several reports have demonstrated that sugar and sugar-related compounds have anti-melanogenic effects on melanocytes [54]. Sung Hoon Lee et al. (2020) found that glucose, a simple sugar, potently decreased intracellular tyrosinase activity in melanocytes. In simple words, this just means that sugar can reduce the melanin content in melanocytes by suppressing the main enzyme responsible for melanogenesis: tyrosinase. This should come as no surprise, as most of us are aware of the dangers of a high sugar diet to our health. However, what they found with regards to cosmetics might surprise you. They discovered that glucose is used as a whitening agent as well as moisturizing ingredient in cosmetics. This is confirmed by various cosmetic websites that list ingredients of products. On one website, cosmeticsinfo.org, it states that glucose may be used in the formulation of bath products, cleansing products, eye makeup, skin care products, makeup and hair care products. This means that many women (and men) could potentially be inhibiting the melanogenesis process by what they put on their face and in their hair.

Melanogenesis Step-By-Step

I've put together a simplified step-by-step process of melanogenesis from start to finish. Study these steps and think to yourself ways in which each step could be disrupted, leading to your melanin not being produced optimally. It must be emphasised that this is the process of producing skin melanin only. Brain melanin, according to Dr. Frank Barr et al. (and various other scientific studies) is capable of self-synthesis. In other words, neuromelanin doesn't go through the same melanogenesis process as eumelanin and pheomelanin, it can apparently produce itself. There's some controversy around the validity of this, however for the sake of simplicity just remember that the melanogenesis process I have described in this chapter is specific to the production of eumelanin and pheomelanin.

Internal & External Regulators

STEP 1: Sunlight (external regulator)
STEP 2: Ocular Melatonin (relies on sunlight)
STEP 3: Pineal Gland (relies on sunlight)
STEP 4: Serotonin (relies on sunlight)
STEP 5: Melatonin (internal regulator, relies on serotonin production and darkness)
STEP 6: Pituitary Gland (relies on melatonin production)
STEP 7: α-MSH (relies on melatonin release)
STEP 8: Melanocytes (relies on α-MSH)
STEP 9: Melanin (relies on melanosomes inside melanocytes)

Please note that each step relies on the step(s) before it to continue the process of producing melanin (MELANOGENESIS). Any step that is blocked, delayed or hindered in any way will result in less melanin production.

Perhaps now after reviewing the step-by-step process of melanogenesis, you'll start to realise why so many people struggle with natural sunlight. Even those with darker skin are now complaining about the sun. Why is this? The melanogenesis process is being disrupted or hindered in some way, leading to sub-optimal melanin production.

Things That Affect Melanogenesis:

- Wearing shades affects melanogenesis
- Staying indoors affects melanogenesis
- Covering your skin from exposure to UV rays affects melanogenesis
- Putting cosmetics on your skin and chemicals in your hair affects melanogenesis
- A high sugar diet affects melanogenesis
- Going to bed late and not getting a good night's sleep affects melanogenesis
- Blue light from smartphones, tablets and laptops affects melanogenesis

All of these things can impact on how much melanin your melanocytes produce. Additionally, studies have shown that certain types of medication can have an impact too. The popular antidiabetic drug metformin has been shown to have an inhibitory effect on melanogenesis [55,56]. This is quite interesting to note as its inhibitory effect on melanogenesis is not listed as one of its side effects. Maybe those who suffer from type 2 diabetes might like to know this information. They may also like to know about the negative effects of sugar on melanogenesis. You now know that high blood sugar levels severely inhibit the production of melanin. Type 2 diabetes can then be used as a good indication of a disrupted melanogenic process.

Melanogenesis and Sunscreen

Other than type 2 diabetes, what else might indicate weak melanin production? Well if we follow logic, a good indicator would be how much natural sunlight you can or can't take. If you're a eumelanin-dominant person who 'can't take the sun' or gets burnt easily when out in the sun, this could potentially be an indication of a disrupted melanogenesis process. What's the solution? Many believe its sunscreen. If you burn easily when out in the sun you may choose to wear sunscreen for protection. However, does wearing sunscreen solve the problem? Well, let's look at this scientifically. Melanin absorbs UV radiation leading to more melanin production. Sunscreen blocks UV radiation, lowering the risk of sunburn. Anything that blocks UV radiation will disrupt melanogenesis. Plus, there are additional risks that come with wearing sunscreen. Studies have repeatedly shown that many sunscreen products contain cancer-causing ingredients [57]. In 2021, a pharmaceutical testing company tested nearly 300 sunscreen products and found 27 percent of them contained benzene. Exposure to higher levels of benzene is known to cause cancer in humans, especially blood cancer, including leukaemia.

"Benzene is one of the most studied and concerning human carcinogens known to science. Its association with forming blood cancers in humans has been shown in numerous studies at trace levels of parts per million and below. The presence of this known human carcinogen in products widely recommended for the prevention of skin cancer and that are regularly used by adults and children is very troubling," -David Light, Founder and CEO of Valisure.

High amounts of benzene in any cosmetic product designed for the skin would be dangerous and detrimental to melanogenesis. Surprisingly, the same testing company also found that hand sanitizers contain trace amounts of this cancer causing chemical [58]. The National Institute for Occupational Safety and Health (NIOSH) defines benzene as a dangerous carcinogen and lists "inhalation, skin absorption, ingestion, skin and/or eye contact" as exposure routes. The US Food and Drug Administration (FDA) states that benzene should not be used in the manufacture of any component of a drug product because of its unacceptable toxicity; however, to meet the high demand for hand sanitizers during the COVID-19 pandemic, the FDA allowed an interim limit of 2 parts per million (ppm) for benzene only in aqueous solution (liquid) hand sanitizers. Of the 260 hand sanitizer products tested by Valisure, including liquid and non-liquid products, 44 batches (17%) contained benzene with the highest level of benzene detected of 16.1ppm, which is over eight times this interim limit.

Valisure are not the only ones who have reported on the cancer-causing chemicals found in skin products such as sunscreen. According to a Daily Mail article from 2019, chemicals in sunscreen get absorbed into your blood at concentrations up to 419 times higher than what is considered safe [59]. In the news article, they say that the chemical oxybenzone reaches plasma concentrations of up to 209.6ng/mL. This is despite the FDA recommending no more than 0.5ng/mL to prevent cancer. While sunscreens are an over the counter drug in the U.S., they are considered cosmetics in the EU. So drugs and cosmetics can negatively impact our skin and our health in dangerous ways. This is science, and not my opinion. So sunscreen users should really consider these findings. Now, if they were to remove the cancer-causing ingredients from all sunscreen products there would still be an obvious issue to consider.

The main external regulator of melanogenesis is UV radiation, and sunscreen is designed to block these light frequencies. So on one hand it's protecting you from sunburn, but on the other hand it's disrupting the melanogenesis process. Now let's be clear, does wearing sunscreen stop the process altogether? No! That's highly unlikely as no sunscreen on the market (as of yet) blocks out 100% of UV radiation. So those who feel like they need to use sunscreen to protect their skin from 'harmful' UV rays, by all means do what's best for you and your skin health. It won't stop the production of melanin from melanocytes, although your melanocytes may not produce as much as they should, leading to a decrease in your melanin's ability to interact with sunlight. For those who are interested in more of a natural solution to UV radiation issues, what would be an alternative way to strengthen the skin to ensure it stays healthy and improve your melanin's ability to interact with sunlight? There are various things that can be done, which are listed under *MARSHALL'S MELANIN TIPS* at the back of this book. But one of the easiest things we can all do is cut down on sugar and start consuming the right foods for melanin. These foods should be from plant sources, as the body needs the right combination of nutrients which only the plants provide. For example, there are certain types of amino acids in plants that absorb UV light. They are called Aromatic Amino Acids (AAA). If you are not consuming AAA's you might struggle to absorb UV light, leading to the classic case of a dark skinned person complaining that they got burnt whilst out in the sun. These amino acids are essential to the melanogenesis process and I will cover them in detail in the next chapter.

Melanin Quiz 5 – Melanogenesis

1 What is melanogenesis?
    A.   The type of cancer that develops in the skin
    B.   The feeling of pensive sadness, typically with no obvious cause
    C.   The complex process of how melanin is produced
    D.   The first book of the Bible

2 Melanogenesis inside of the melanosome starts with what amino acid?
    A.   Tryptophan
    B.   Tyrosine
    C.   Cysteine
    D.   Arginine

3 Which enzyme speeds up the production of melanin?
    A.   Lactase
    B.   Lipase
    C.   Cellulase
    D.   Tyrosinase

4 Pheomelanin naturally has more of an acidic pH due to the presence of what amino acid in its molecular structure?
    A.   Histidine
    B.   Cysteine
    C.   Tyrosine
    D.   Glutamine

5 Which gland plays a primary role in the process of melanogenesis?
    A.   Prostate Gland
    B.   Sweat Gland
    C.   Salivary Gland
    D.   Pineal Gland

6 Which hormone, secreted by the pineal gland, regulates melanogenesis?
    A.   Serotonin
    B.   Melatonin
    C.   Testosterone
    D.   Estrogen

7 Other than cell repair at night, what other functions are attributed to melatonin?

A. Dream Regulation
B. Immune Activity Regulation
C. Reproduction and Fertility Regulation
D. All the above

8 Although melatonin is known as the hormone of darkness, it is first produced in the ____ during daylight

A. Eyes
B. Nose
C. Ears
D. Mouth

9 Which of the following can negatively affect the process of melanogenesis?

A. No skin exposure to ultraviolet radiation
B. Blue light from smartphones and laptops
C. High blood sugar
D. All the above

10 If UV radiation is needed for the production of melanin, what would wearing sunscreen do to melanogenesis?

A. Initiate the process
B. Disrupt the process
C. Reverse the process
D. Enhance the process

CHAPTER SIX

FOODS FOR MELANIN

FOODS FOR MELANIN

What should I eat for melanin? This is one of the most frequent questions I get asked when I teach adults about melanin. It's a valid question to ask, considering the vital role the food we eat plays in the production of melanin (melanogenesis). Due to the miseducation we've all had, many people are unaware of just how important what we eat is to our melanin, and how certain foods can accelerate or decelerate the melanogenesis process. Hopefully this chapter will bring you clarity and act as a reference point for years to come. Now, instead of me just giving you a list of foods to eat and foods to avoid I'd like you to think about what you've learnt from reading this book so far. You've learnt that everyone has melanin. You've learnt that there are two main types of hair and skin melanin. The two main types are eumelanin and pheomelanin. Eumelanin is the black and brown pigment, whilst pheomelanin is the red and yellow pigment. Eumelanin has a much broader absorption spectrum than pheomelanin, hence the reason why darker skinned individuals tend to be more protected when out in the sun due to their melanin's ability to absorb and dissipate sunlight energy. The body utilises this sunlight energy in a similar way to how plants utilise it for photosynthesis (by splitting the water molecule into hydrogen and oxygen). You've also learnt that the visible light frequencies from the sun are absorbed and reflected in different amounts by plant pigments resulting in the different colours we see in nature. Keeping this in mind, let's cover what types of foods are best for melanin.

Full Spectrum

We have already covered the fact that pheomelanin requires more Vitamin A type foods, which are found in red, orange and yellow fruits and vegetables to help with the production of the red and yellow type of pigment. So let's now focus on foods for eumelanin. There doesn't seem to be many black and brown coloured foods in nature to match the colour of eumelanin, so what would be best for the most common type of hair and skin melanin? Well, understanding that eumelanin absorbs all visible light frequencies, from red all the way to violet should answer this question. Eumelanin requires the full spectrum of light to function optimally (ROY-G-BIV). Therefore, all the different coloured fruits and vegetables are needed for a eumelanin diet. "Eat the rainbow" is a common phrase that summarises this point. However, the darker the fruits and vegetables the better, due to higher antioxidant content. So look for fruits and vegetables from the BIV section of the spectrum, because we tend to be bombarded with the ROY colours when we go to the supermarket. Let's be clear though, there is nothing wrong with consuming the ROY coloured fruits and vegetables. However, eumelanin requires the full spectrum of colours for optimal health, so the darker coloured fruits and vegetables (anthocyanins) need to play a big part in your diet as well. These dark coloured fruits and vegetables will be high in antioxidants such as Vitamins A, C and E, polyphenols, glutathione precursors, digestive enzymes and essential minerals. The darker coloured fruits in particular will not only be high in antioxidants, but will also be high in a plant compound called resveratrol.

Resveratrol

There have been numerous studies highlighting the benefits of resveratrol, found in large amounts in the skin of dark red and purple grapes. It has been known to have a positive effect on the circulatory system by lowering cholesterol, protecting the skin from oxidative damage leading to a more youthful appearance, and enhancing male testosterone by boosting metabolism. But why is resveratrol important in the production of melanin? Well, resveratrol is the plant version of the main amino acid tyrosine. If you recall from the *MELANOGENESIS* chapter, tyrosine is the precursor to melanin. Put simply, resveratrol is like tyrosine in plants. Studies have shown that resveratrol mimics tyrosine [60], so it can trigger the start of melanogenesis in the same way that tyrosine does. Where can you find resveratrol? The following food sources are high in resveratrol

Mulberries	**Red Grapes**
Billberries	**Purple / Black Grapes**
Blueberries	**Raw Cacao***
Cranberries	**Red Wine***

*Now, please don't go on a red wine binge thinking that red wine is healthy. It's not my intention to create a nation of scientific alcoholics (or chocoholics for that matter). The reason why resveratrol is high in red wine is because red wine is made from dark grapes, like the purple to black variety that were mentioned in a previous chapter. Resveratrol is actually found in the skin of the grapes, the darker the skin the more resveratrol it contains. The raw cacao bean also contains resveratrol, giving hope to chocolate lovers everywhere. However, please note that the antioxidant effects are with the raw cacao bean and not the processed cocoa used to make chocolate bars. In other words, the health benefits of resveratrol are in the natural beans that chocolate is made from, not so much the chocolate itself; just like the health benefits of red wine come from the natural grapes used to make the red wine, not so much the wine itself. Either way, getting more resveratrol into your diet may prove to be very beneficial. Studies have found resveratrol to be anti-aging, anti-tumor, anti-inflammatory and antimicrobial [61]. It has also been found to boost the immune system, improve brain function and fight cancer [62]. Look for the anthocyanin pigment in fruits and vegetables to ensure you're getting your daily dose of this tyrosine-type of plant compound.

Selenium

You will also need to look for foods high in selenium. Selenium is one of the most powerful antioxidant minerals found inside the human body. Although it is not directly part of the eumelanin chemical pathway it does assist melanin in various ways. You'll find that wherever there's eumelanin in the body there will also be selenium close by. This is because there are actually selenium-specific proteins, appropriately named selenoproteins, which aid in the production and protection of skin cells. In fact, studies have shown that selenoproteins are essential for proper keratinocyte function and skin development [63]. Thus, foods high in selenium will no doubt be beneficial to melanin. The problem is however, selenium has become a very scarce mineral in soil in many parts of the world. This means that it's becoming more and more difficult to find quality food sources of selenium in plants. Selenium is critical to the health of all living organisms. It has been postulated that the vast majority of the world's population has suboptimal selenium intakes, and hence is at increased risk of several diseases such as cancer, heart disease, viral diseases and other conditions that involve increased levels of oxidative stress [64]. Although there seems to be a global selenium deficiency, you might still be able to get adequate amounts in sea vegetables (algae) like sea moss and bladderwrack. The added benefit of including these types of foods in your diet is that they tend to be high in essential fatty acids as well. Essential Fatty Acids (EFA's) are necessary for the following processes:

- Formation of healthy cell membranes
- Proper development and functioning of the brain and nervous system
- Proper thyroid and adrenal activity
- Hormone synthesis
- Regulation of blood pressure and cholesterol
- Regulation of immune and inflammatory responses
- Regulation of blood clotting
- Supports healthy skin and hair

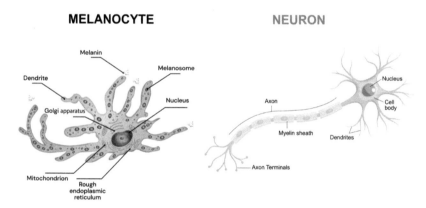

Figure 26
Melanocyte / neuron comparison

PUFA's Omega 6 and 3

The two main EFA's are linoleic acid (omega-6) and alpha-linoleic acid (omega-3). These polyunsaturated fats or PUFA's (Polyunsaturated Fatty Acids) are known as essential because your body cannot produce them on its own, so they must come from your diet. As individuals become more health conscious, the knowledge and awareness around the effects of PUFA's on a cellular level become more apparent. What remains a mystery however, is the link between PUFA's and melanocytes. What effect do they have on melanin? PUFA's are crucial to the optimal functioning of the nervous system due to their positive effect on dendrites. Dendrites are tree-like extensions at the beginning of neurons (nerve cells) that receive signals (information) from other neurons. If you take a look at **Figure 26** you'll see a typical melanocyte

83

side by side with a typical neuron of the nervous system. Notice the similarities, especially in the way that the dendrites extend from the cell body. Polyunsaturated fatty acids are vital to the health of dendritic cells. A deficiency in PUFA's could result in shortened dendrites. This would severely compromise the melanocytes ability to distribute melanin far and wide throughout the body. According to a number of published papers on this topic it seems to be Omega-3 fatty acids that have the most modulatory effect on dendrites [65]. This may be due to its well-publicised anti-inflammatory properties. Omega-3 fatty acids can reduce the production of molecules and substances linked to inflammation [66]. Scientific studies have consistently observed a connection between higher omega-3 intake and reduced inflammation [67]. The evidence suggests that consuming more foods high in omega-3 would be beneficial for those looking to reduce inflammation in the body. What foods are high in omega-3? Here's a list of ten omega-3 rich foods.

1. Chia Seeds
2. Flax Seeds
3. Mackerel
4. Salmon
5. Walnuts
6. Cod Liver Oil
7. Sardines
8. Herring
9. Shellfish (Oysters)
10. Hemp Seeds

Looking at this list you'll find that many of the food sources high in omega-3 come from oily fish. Yes, fish tends to be one of the highest sources of omega-3 fatty acids. However, due to an increase in fish containing heavy metals, mercury, dioxins, plastic compounds, hexachlorobenzenes and PCBs, it might not be a great idea to rely on oily fish for your daily dose of omega-3. The obvious question people tend to ask is "If not from fish, where can I get omega-3?" This really should be followed by the logical question of: "Where do the fish get it from?" The answer is simple: ALGAE (sea vegetables or seaweed). Studies suggest that the best source of omega-3 is the same source where the fish get it from, algae [68]. There are different types of algae classified by their colour: brown algae (kelp), green algae (Spirulina and Chlorella) and red algae. Dr. Sebi was famous for promoting the health benefits of a red algae called Chondrus Crispus, a type of sea moss that he used frequently alongside Bladderwrack. It seems the health benefits of consuming Chondrus Crispus, and other types of algae, extend far beyond its high omega-3 content. Studies have shown that seaweed and microalgae are also rich sources of protein and contain all of the essential amino acids at various concentrations [69].

Amino Acids

Amino Acids are the building blocks for proteins. Your body creates its own proteins from the amino acids it needs. There are 20 main amino acids that the body needs to make proteins. Of the 20, most scientists agree that 9 are essential (cannot be made in the body) and 11 are non-essential (can be made in the body). Essential amino acids need to be consumed as part of your diet or the body will not have the necessary building blocks required to make proteins.

Essential Amino Acids
Isoleucine
Leucine
Valine
Phenylalanine (Aromatic Amino Acid, precursor to Tyrosine)
Tryptophan (Aromatic Amino Acid, precursor to Serotonin)
Histidine
Lysine
Threonine
Methionine

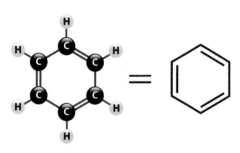

Figure 27
Aromatic ring

Non-Essential Amino Acids
Alanine
Cysteine
Glutamine
Glutamic Acid
Glycine
Serine
Asparagine
Aspartic Acid
Proline
Arginine
Tyrosine (Aromatic Amino Acid, precursor to melanin, synthesised from phenylalanine)

Aromatic Amino Acids

Aromatic Amino Acids (AAA) are amino acids that include an aromatic ring. Aromatic rings trap photons (absorb light). If you were to look at a typical aromatic ring you'll notice that it is shaped like a hexagon (see Figure 27). The hexagon shape is due to 6 carbon atoms forming the ring. In science, this specific formation is called an aromatic ring; and aromatic rings absorb light in the ultraviolet spectrum. There are three Aromatic Amino Acids that have this type of ring.

The three main AAA's are:
1. Tyrosine (tyr)
2. Tryptophan (trp)
3. Phenylalanine (phe)

To different degrees, all Aromatic Amino Acids absorb ultraviolet (UV) light. Due to this fact, AAA's are the key component to how we interact with the sun. The more AAA's present in your diet the better the absorption of UV rays. The less AAA's present in your diet the more problems you may have with the sun. Only plants can synthesize AAA's, animals cannot. So animals, including humans, rely on plants for AAA synthesis. This is the main reason why a full spectrum plant foods diet would be beneficial for melanin.

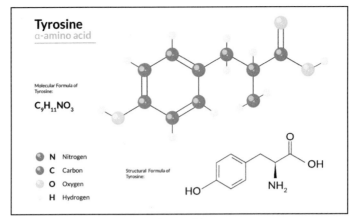

Figure 28
Tyrosine molecular structure

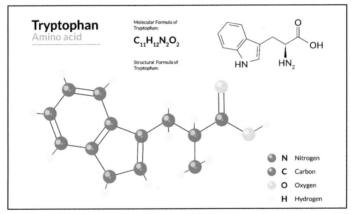

Figure 29
Tryptophan molecular structure

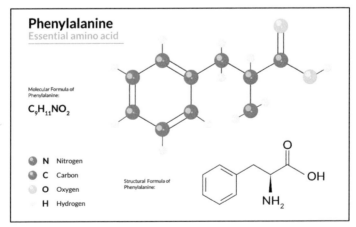

Figure 30
Phenylalanine molecular structure

Copper

What is the link between copper and melanin? Why is copper so important for skin and hair pigmentation? What can a lack of copper in the diet lead to? These are questions I found myself asking when I was researching the best foods for melanin many years ago. I had heard that copper was important for pigmentation but didn't know why. It turns out the answer is quite simple. Tyrosine, the Aromatic Amino Acid responsible for melanin synthesis, relies 100% on the enzyme tyrosinase for melanogenesis. Think of tyrosinase as the key to the ignition of the melanin car. That key needs to be inserted into the ignition and then turned for the car to start. Once that key is turned, a series of things happen inside of the engine and then the car is good to go. However, the car is not even going to start up if the key (tyrosinase) is not available. That's how important tyrosinase is to melanin production; it's like the key to the whole process. What has this got to do with copper? Short answer: Everything! Because that key is made of copper! Yes, tyrosinase is a copper-based enzyme which is absolutely crucial to the melanogenesis process. How crucial? Well, a copper deficiency has been linked to vitiligo, fatigue and weakness, problems with memory and learning, weak and brittle bones, premature grey hair, frequent sickness, sensitivity to cold and pale skin.

Various studies have shown that copper actually stimulates melanocytes into action, increasing melanin production and re-pigmenting the skin. This is important to know if you are a dark skinned person recovering from any type of skin condition. If you are suffering from any sort of skin abrasion and can see that the new skin coming through is of a lighter hue, more copper in your diet could aid in darkening that area and bringing your complexion back to its natural state. For example, those who suffer terribly from eczema, there might've been a time when a doctor prescribed a steroid cream to help ease the itching. Although the steroid cream may have calmed your symptoms, you may have noticed that your skin started to lighten up due to the steroid in the cream. Increasing your intake of copper should help to bring back your original colour. Going by that logic, the opposite must be true too. If someone wanted to intentionally lighten their skin, they could reduce their intake of copper or use tyrosinase inhibitors, which block tyrosinase activity.

It should be noted here that tyrosinase is not just responsible for melanogenesis in humans, but for melanin formation in all life domains. Therefore, anything that inhibits the activity of tyrosinase in any living organism will result in a loss or degradation of melanin in that organism. In the medical industry tyrosinase inhibitors are used for the prevention of severe hyperpigmentation and other skin disorders. In the cosmetics industry tyrosinase inhibitors are used in skin-whitening creams (or bleaching creams as they are widely known); and in agriculture they are used to prevent fruit browning. Numerous studies indicate that continued use of such inhibitors is unsafe. Especially the two main types used in skin whitening creams called hydroquinone (HQ) and Kojic Acid (KA). Hydroquinone is a very powerful, well-studied whitening agent, which is extensively used in leading cosmetic hyperpigmentation treatments, and over-the-counter cosmetics like dark spot erasers, age spot removers and melasma products. Any products that contain as little as 2% HQ or KA are likely to have an effect on tyrosinase activity and therefore melanin production. It may surprise you to know that both HQ and KA are found in small amounts in certain foods. Here's a list of foods that contain them.

Foods that contain HQ:

- Wheat Products
- Wheat Cereals
- White Bread
- White Pasta
- Pears
- Coffee
- Tea

<u>Foods that contain KA:</u>

- Soy Sauce
- Soya Beans
- Soybean Paste
- Soy Vegan Products*

Most soy products contain potent tyrosinase inhibitors which have six times the anti-tyrosinase activity of kojic acid

All of these foods will decrease tyrosinase activity leading to less melanin production. To boost tyrosinase activity you will need more copper in your diet. But not just any copper obviously, as pure copper is a metal. This reddish-gold coloured metal is ductile, malleable, and an effective conductor of heat and electricity. Pure copper is the second best metal conductor of electricity behind silver. Due to its high conductivity characteristic copper wires are the most frequently used wires inside of electrical cables. Any electric cable you have in your home probably has a copper wire running through it. This is not the type of copper you need to consume for your biological requirements, of course not. So, what type of copper do you need and where does it come from? You need bioavailable copper or simply put, copper your body can assimilate. And as copper is a naturally occurring element, it can be found pretty much everywhere. It's present in the earth's crust, in oceans, lakes, rivers, and plants. It is actually the plants that make the copper "bioavailable" to us. The plants convert it into a form that humans can digest and assimilate. Plants do this with iron as well, another metal. The plants soak up the iron from the mineral-rich soil from which they grow and process it into a bioavailable source for human consumption. This is why it's better to get your vitamins and minerals directly from plants for optimal assimilation.

Caution

I will now present to you a list of foods that would be beneficial for eumelanin, based on the science you have learned from this book. Please note that these food sources should be from non-GMO crop and therefore 100% natural, fresh and organic. Unfortunately, the use of genetically modified crops and seeds is now very much the norm, so finding the foods listed here in their natural unmodified state will be difficult. To make matters worse, nowadays nearly all fruits and vegetables are sprayed with pesticides. Research by The Soil Association has found that most produce have up to 32 different pesticides sprayed on them. This toxic chemical mixture could be harmful to human health, even if the food is considered "healthy." As a representative from the Pesticide Action Network UK group once pointed out, "Mainstream agriculture in the UK looks less like farming and more like chemistry. The British public simply isn't aware of how many different chemicals are being used to grow our food." This is unfortunately the new normal worldwide, so we need to ensure that the produce we do buy is pesticide-free (highly unlikely) or that we know how to wash the pesticides off after purchase. Salt water, sodium bicarbonate (baking soda) and apple cider vinegar have all been shown to be effective. These days hardly any food we eat can be considered 100% healthy, unless we grew it ourselves. So we must remain cautious and conscious of what we are eating.

Be cautious of language too; especially the term "plant-based" as many vegan food options are now being stuffed with chemicals to make them taste like the plants they are mimicking. "Plant-based" unfortunately doesn't mean plant food. For example, the vegan burgers offered by popular fast food outlets are considered "plant-based." These burgers are full of chemicals, estrogen and tyrosinase inhibitors. We must look to full spectrum plant foods for health and healing properties; and not "plant-based" foods created in a laboratory to trick our taste buds. With that being said, this list is based on full spectrum plant foods being in their natural state. Keep this in mind as you go through the list.

Foods for Eumelanin

Foods high in AAA's and antioxidants: Vitamins A, C, E
- Dark Green Leafy Vegetables
- Apples, Oranges, Apricots
- Star Fruit, Jackfruit, Kiwifruit
- Mangoes, Papayas, Pineapple
- Avocados, Figs, Watermelon
- Dates, Dandelion Greens, Guava
- Grapefruit, Lemons, Key Limes

Foods high in resveratrol and anthocyanins
- Bilberries
- Blueberries
- Blackberries
- Elderberries
- Mulberries
- Black / Purple Grapes
- Red Grapes
- Raw Cacao

Foods high in tyrosine
- Chlorella and Spirulina
- Pumpkin Seeds
- Hemp Seeds
- Sesame Seeds
- Coconut Water
- Quinoa and Wild Rice
- Teff and Kamut
- Moringa Leaves

Foods high in copper
- Dark Green Leafy Vegetables
- Spirulina
- Shiitake Mushrooms
- Seafood
- Almonds
- Cashews
- Sesame Seeds

- Sweet Potatoes
- Avocados
- Chickpeas
- Quinoa
- Chia Seeds
- Dark Chocolate

Foods high in Omega 3
- Hemp Seeds
- Chia Seeds
- Flax Seeds
- Sea Moss
- Wakame
- Walnuts
- Kelp

Foods low in selenium*
- Brazil Nuts
- Mushrooms
- Sea Vegetables / Algae (sea moss and bladderwrack)

Selenium is a very scarce mineral in soil all over the world, so foods that do contain selenium will only have it in low amounts

All of these food sources come directly from plants. Consuming plant foods would be best for eumelanin because it is the plants that make essential nutrients like copper and iron bioavailable. Also, only plants can synthesise AAA's. Some may say, "Well, why can't I get my amino acids from the meat I eat?" When you consume animal meat your body has to break down the animal proteins into the individual amino acids that your cells require. This is an energy-depleting process for your digestive system. It is also a very long process, as some doctors believe that the human digestive system can take up to 72 hours to digest meat [70]. Your body needs amino acids to build proteins, not the other way around. The way we've been taught about proteins is so confusing, and somewhat backwards to how the human body works. We've been taught to believe that we need protein from our diet as it's an essential nutrient. The body doesn't need protein for nourishment. The body needs amino acids to formulate its own proteins required by the cells for cellular processes. Proteins do most of the work in cells and are required for the structure, function, and regulation of the body's tissues and organs. Enzymes, which are made of proteins, speed up cellular processes in the body. Your melanin relies on the cellular process of melanogenesis; and melanogenesis cannot occur without the presence of the three main AAA's of Tryptophan, Phenylalanine and Tyrosine. Tyrosine is the precursor to Melanin and Phenylalanine is the precursor to Tyrosine.

No Phenylalanine? No Tyrosine!
No Tyrosine? No Melanin!

Where do we get Phenylalanine from? Plants! These three aromatic amino acids are so important to the absorption of UV light that they need to be a part of our diet in order for our melanin to function optimally. Tryptophan is the precursor to Serotonin and Serotonin gets converted to Melatonin at night. Therefore…

90

No Tryptophan? No Serotonin
No Serotonin? No Melatonin
No Melatonin? No Melanogenesis

Where do we get Tryptophan from? Plants! Thus, melanogenesis is entirely dependent on these three aromatic amino acids.

Foods for Pheomelanin

Fruits and Vegetables high in Vitamin A
- Carrots
- Sweet Potatoes
- Red Peppers
- Pumpkin
- Apricots
- Spinach
- Beets

Cruciferous Vegetables (high in sulphur)
- Arugula
- Bok Choy
- Broccoli
- Brussel Sprouts
- Cabbage
- Cauliflower
- Horseradish
- Kale
- Turnips

Allium Vegetables (high in sulphur)
- Garlic
- Leeks
- Onions
- Scallions
- Shallots

Once again, notice that all the recommendations are from plant sources. These plant sources are high in AAA's, sulphur and of course the essential nutrient for pheomelanin: Vitamin A. Just so you know, there are animal sources of vitamin A too. Contrary to popular belief vitamin A is not a single vitamin. Instead, it encompasses two families of compounds called retinoids and carotenoids. Beta-Carotene is the plant version of vitamin A, which is part of the carotenoid family. The majority of food sources recommended here for pheomelanin are from the carotenoid family. Retinol is one of the retinoid compounds found mainly in meat, which could be classified as the animal-based version of vitamin A. Retinol can be found in high amounts in foods like beef liver, cod liver oil, eggs, lamb liver, whole milk, butter, tuna, cheese and chicken. Due to the presence of retinol, which is easily absorbed by the body, these types of foods may prove to be beneficial for pheomelanin-dominant individuals. A eumelanin-dominant individual needs more vitamin D than vitamin A, as sunlight is its number one nutrient. Melanin ingests sunlight like food, so no sun exposure would be like starving melanin of its main food source. This wouldn't be good for anyone's health, according to the evidence. There have been numerous published papers warning us of the dangers of inadequate sun exposure for many years. In a recent review paper, Lars Alfredsson et al. clearly explain the benefits of sun exposure and the consequences from a lack of sunshine. They even went so far as to say that insufficient sun exposure is a significant public health problem [71]. Here is part of their abstract:

> *"This article aims to alert the medical community and public health authorities to accumulating evidence on health benefits from sun exposure, which suggests that insufficient sun exposure is a significant public health problem. Studies in the past decade indicate that insufficient sun exposure may be responsible for 340,000 deaths in the United States and 480,000 deaths in Europe per year, and an increased incidence of breast cancer, colorectal cancer, hypertension, cardiovascular disease, metabolic syndrome, multiple sclerosis, Alzheimer's disease, autism, asthma, type 1 diabetes and myopia. Vitamin D has long been considered the principal mediator of beneficial effects of sun exposure. However, oral vitamin D supplementation has not been convincingly shown to prevent the above conditions; thus, serum 25(OH)D as an indicator of vitamin D status may be a proxy for and not a mediator of beneficial effects of sun exposure. New candidate mechanisms include the release of nitric oxide from the skin and direct effects of ultraviolet radiation (UVR) on peripheral blood cells. Collectively, this evidence indicates it would be wise for people living outside the tropics to ensure they expose their skin sufficiently to the sun."*

In this paper, there's some scientific jargon that may be slightly confusing for the lay person. However, I'm sure you get the gist of the abstract, which is that vitamin D is definitely needed to prevent the diseases they mentioned and according to their research vitamin D supplementation *"has not been convincingly shown to prevent the above conditions."* Relying on food for adequate vitamin D levels would be futile as well, because only small quantities of vitamin D are present in any natural food source, including vitamin D-fortified foods [72]. So what does this mean for the eumelanin-dominant individual? Feed your melanin with sunlight!

Melanin Quiz 6 – Foods for Melanin

1 What colour fruits would be best for melanin?
- A. ROY coloured fruits
- B. G coloured fruits
- C. BIV coloured fruits
- D. ROY-G-BIV (full spectrum of colours)

2 Resveratrol, a plant compound that mimics tyrosine, can typically be found in the skin of?
- A. Chickens and Turkeys
- B. Dark Red and Purple Grapes
- C. Cows and Pigs
- D. Pork chops and Beef liver

3 Studies have found Resveratrol to be?
- A. Anti-aging and Anti-tumor
- B. Anti-inflammatory
- C. Antimicrobial
- D. All the above

4 Which vital antioxidant mineral is essential for proper functioning of skin?
- A. Selenium
- B. Sulphur
- C. Fluoride
- D. Benzene

5 What type of essential fatty acid (EFA) would be most beneficial for those looking to reduce inflammation in the body?
- A. Omega-9 (Oleic Acid)
- B. Omega-6 (Linoleic Acid)
- C. Omega-3 (Alpha-Linoleic Acid)
- D. Omega-7 (Palmitoleic Acid)

6 Studies suggest that the best source of omega-3 is?
- A. Fish Oils
- B. Algae
- C. Mackerel
- D. Sardines

7 What are aromatic amino acids (AAA)?
- A. Amino acids that include an aromatic ring, shaped like a square
- B. Amino acids that include an aromatic ring, shaped like a hexagon
- C. Amino acids that include an aromatic ring, shaped like a triangle
- D. Amino acids that include an aromatic ring, shaped like a circle

8 **AAA's from plant sources would be beneficial for melanin because of their ability to?**
   A.   Absorb UV light
   B.   Block UV light
   C.   Reflect UV light
   D.   Refract UV light

9 **Which one of the following is not an AAA?**
   A.   Phenylalanine (phe)
   B.   Tryptophan (trp)
   C.   Tyrosine (tyr)
   D.   Cysteine (cys)

10 **What vitamin do eumelanin-dominant individuals need more of?**
   A.   D
   B.   C
   C.   B
   D.   A

11 **What Vitamin in particular increases pheomelanin?**
   A.   Vitamin D
   B.   Vitamin C
   C.   Vitamin A
   D.   Vitamin E

12 **What is the most reliable way to increase vitamin D in the body?**
   A.   Putting on sunscreen
   B.   Exposing your skin to the sun
   C.   Wearing lots of clothes and staying indoors
   D.   Taking Vitamin D supplements

CHAPTER SEVEN

WATER FOR MELANIN

WATER FOR MELANIN

What is the best water to drink for melanin? This is a very important question to answer, as all living cells inside of your body require water to operate, including melanocytes. Proper hydration, detoxification, and oxygen are key to melanin health. Water makes up over 70% of the human body, making it the most important substance in your body. There's no way you can properly hydrate if you don't have enough water inside and outside of your cells. Without adequate and complete hydration, the brain, tissues, organs, and muscles cannot function at their full potential. Without adequate and complete hydration, the body cannot utilise amino acids to build the necessary proteins it needs for cellular functions. Put simply, hydration is the key to health! Nothing in your body functions dry (make a mental note of this). Every cell in your body needs to be hydrated to continually carry out biochemical reactions. The dryer the cell the more resistant it is to an electric current. Without water the cells dry out and become dehydrated. Dehydration is directly linked to ageing. The more dehydrated you are, the faster you age. It's that simple. If your cells are drying out, they're dying out! This can't be emphasised enough: Hydration is key to the health of your melanin.

So what water should we be drinking for proper hydration? If you listen to modern day health "Gurus" who have huge followings online, they'd probably tell you to drink alkaline water, ionized water, mineralized water, distilled water, filtered water, purified water or some type of electrolysis machine water. It's all very confusing; and the confusion surrounding water is at an all-time high, leading to many people seeking answers online to aid in their decisions about what water to drink for health. This can be challenging for the average person, having to manoeuvre their way around all the mixed messages and misinformation surrounding water in this technological day and age. It's like a minefield of misinformation for one to diligently navigate to find the truth about water. Should we be drinking bottled water? Dr. Sebi approved alkaline water? Expensive machine-making water or just tap?! As always, the answers to life's mysteries tend to be simple. The type of water that we should be drinking for melanin is water that nature has provided for us. The water that comes from plants and springs is natures' water or 'living' water; and what makes this type of water beneficial for us is its interaction with the sun. This interaction with the sun creates a type of water commonly known as structured water.

Structured Water

What is structured water? This is where nature's water molecules are energised by heat and sunlight creating an 'order' or lattice 'structure' within the water. The lattice structure is due to the water molecule being separated (split) into positively charged hydrogen ions (H^+) and negatively charged oxygen ions (OH^-). In science, when the water molecule splits into positive and negative charges the negatively charged ions are called hydroxide ions, as one oxygen atom is still bonded to one hydrogen atom (see Figure 31).

96

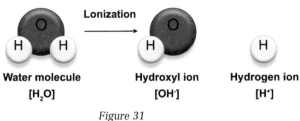

Water molecule
[H₂O]

Hydroxyl ion
[OH⁻]

Hydrogen ion
[H⁺]

Lonization

Figure 31
Water dissociation

This split also separates or 'excludes' all impurities from the negatively charged water, hence it is sometimes known as Exclusion Zone water or EZ water. Dr. Gerald Pollack, a professor at the University of Washington and considered by most to be the leading authority on structured water, has been studying water science and technologies for over two decades. He believes that water is profoundly impacted by light and heat-generating sources found in nature, which change the molecular composition of the water we drink and store within our bodies. Water in nature is naturally structured even though you can't see any form in it. At a molecular level, under a microscope EZ water has a shape that is organized in a specific geometric pattern similar to a hexagonal crystal lattice.

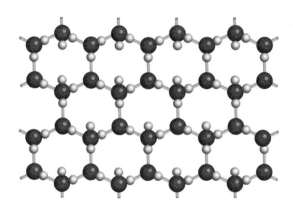

Figure 32
Hexagonal crystalline lattice structure

Water from springs, waterfalls and glaciers are structured. The water in fruits and vegetables is naturally structured by sunlight. This is the main reason why drinking the juice from fresh fruits and vegetables is so healthy for you. You're drinking EZ water! This type of water is in all living organisms — from plants, to animals, to you and me. This is very important to note: The water that makes up over 70% of our body is mainly structured (EZ) water and not ordinary water. It is different to ordinary (bulk) water which has a chemical formula of H_2O (two atoms of hydrogen bonded to one atom of oxygen).

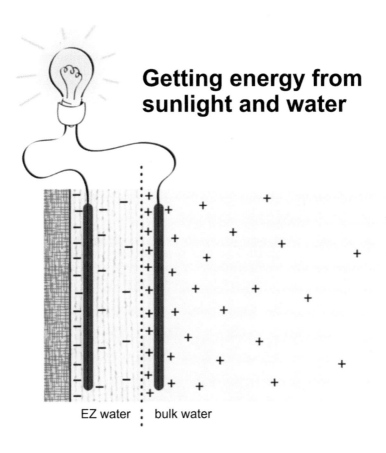

Getting energy from sunlight and water

EZ water ⁝ bulk water

Figure 33
EZ water (charge separation)

Fourth Phase of Water

According to Dr. Gerald Pollack, there are actually four different phases of water: Solid, Liquid, Gas and Plasma (structured water). The fourth phase is totally different from the three that we were taught in school when we were children (solid, liquid and gas). This fourth phase occurs mainly next to water-loving (hydrophilic) surfaces. Professor Pollack discovered that absorption of sunlight puts water into an electrically active liquid crystal state, and he has found that most of the water in living organisms is in this state. In his book *The Fourth Phase of Water: Beyond Solid, Liquid, and Vapor* he points out how structured water in living organisms is a crystalline H_3O_2 structure, not H_2O. He calls it EZ water, standing for "Exclusion Zone" because the water excludes impurities as it orders itself (see Figure 33).

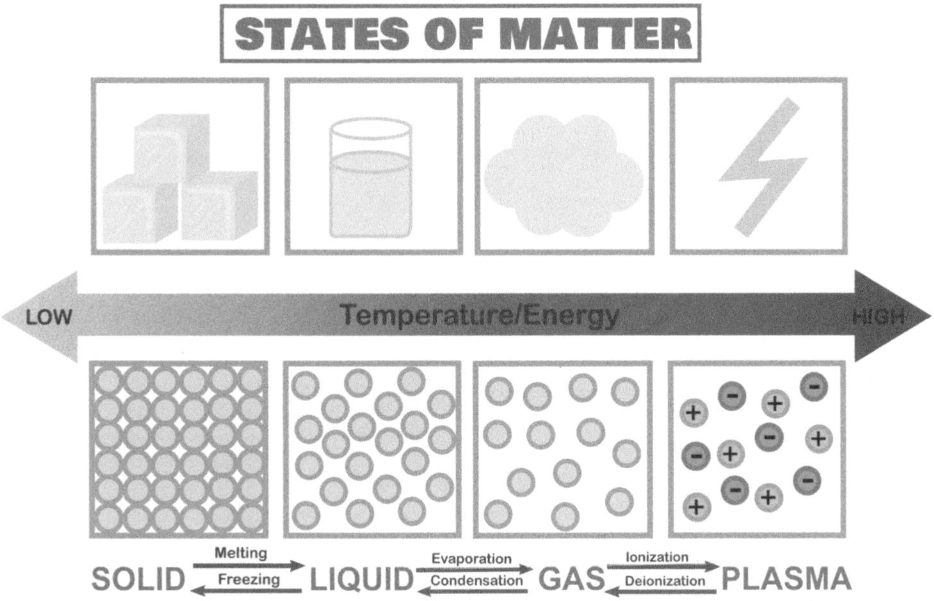

STATES OF MATTER

LOW → Temperature/Energy → HIGH

SOLID ⇄ (Melting/Freezing) LIQUID ⇄ (Evaporation/Condensation) GAS ⇄ (Ionization/Deionization) PLASMA

Figure 34
States of Matter

The energy for this 'ordering' or 'structuring' comes from sunlight and heat. The heat (in the form of infrared) changes the water from a random H_2O orientation to a uniform, electron-sharing stack, resembling a hexagonal crystalline lattice structure. This is the type of water that energises your cells. This H_3O_2 water, sometimes called gel water, is in between a solid and a liquid. An extra hydrogen atom and an extra oxygen atom make it denser than H_2O and highly viscous (gel-like). This is why water doesn't come gushing out of you like a hose if you cut yourself. Your cells are filled with this thicker, H_3O_2 type of water. Dr. Pollack coined the term Exclusion Zone water or EZ water because he recognized that the H_3O_2 in your body was able to exclude even the smallest particles. In short, this means that the water in your body can act like a natural filter. If the water in your body is acting like a filter, then it's preventing impurities from penetrating your cells. The health benefits of this at a cellular level are highly significant and should be quite obvious to you. Keeping your cells free from harmful impurities is the essence of disease prevention. What Dr. Gerald Pollack has revealed to us through his extensive work is that if we want to get our bodies back into alignment with nature and health, we need to be hydrating our cells with structured (EZ) water.

ORDINARY WATER   STRUCTURED WATER

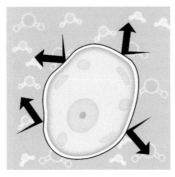 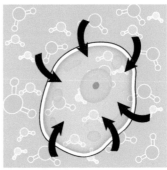

Figure 35
Structured Water Entering Cells

What Creates Structured Water?

Infrared light has been shown to be the most effective at creating structured water. More than half the sun's power output is in the form of infrared light. This infrared light creates the exclusion zone by organising charge within the water into layers of negatively charged ions and excreting positively charged ions away from it. What I've gathered from studying Dr. Pollacks' work is that in order for infrared light to do this it needs to interact with a hydrophilic (water loving) surface. In plants, chlorophyll acts as a hydrophilic surface for sunlight to interact with water. In humans, each one of our cells has a membrane that surrounds the cell and regulates what enters and exits the cell. The outside of the cell membrane, which is like the skin of the cell, is known to be hydrophilic. What's very interesting to note is that eumelanin is hydrophilic and its electrical properties are strongly dependent on its hydration state [73]. If everything that Dr. Pollack says about how to create structured water is true, then it sounds to me like eumelanin might just be the best hydrophilic surface needed to do the 'structuring' job. This is something that is not mentioned in any of Dr. Pollacks' published works however, so please just take this as my conjecture.

Based on Dr. Gerald Pollack's work here's what builds structured EZ water in your cells:

- Water – Raw material for building EZ water, therefore you need water in order for the exclusion zone (EZ) to occur inside of it
- Sunshine – More than half of the radiation the sun emits is in the form of Infrared rays. Infrared light creates the exclusion zone
- Green juicing – Plant cell water contains EZ. Therefore, juicing plants (especially green plants) would be a great way to get more structured water inside your cells
- Coconut water – Like green juices, it's already structured, alkaline and highly electric
- Saunas (infrared saunas) – Infrared light builds EZ. Some people use these types of saunas as light therapy for certain diseases. Infrared saunas inside of homes are becoming very popular
- Grounding (earthing) – The earth emits infrared rays and your bare feet absorb the negative ions when they connect with the earth. Negative charge builds EZ

100

Unstructured Water

Is structured water the same as ionized alkaline water? Dr. Pollack has said in the past that ionized alkaline water is similar in properties to structured EZ water. Both have a high pH due to an abundance of negative ions. The chief difference is that this type of alkaline water is made by electrodes in an ionizer, whereas the EZ water inside you is created by healthy activities like basking in the sun, drinking green vegetable juice and walking barefoot on the Earth. The electrodes in many of these alkaline water-making machines perform electrolysis, which is the process of using electricity to dissociate water into positive (H⁺) and negative ions (OH⁻). See Figure 37 for a visual of this. So, what water do you think your cells prefer? Water made from a machine designed to perform electrolysis to split the water molecule into hydrogen and oxygen? Or water structured naturally by chlorophyll and sunlight? This is ultimately the difference between any type of water and structured water. Was it created by the interaction between sunlight and a natural hydrophilic surface like chlorophyll? No? Then it's not structured.

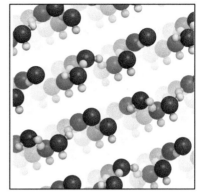

Figure 36
Unstructured Water

Different types of unstructured water

- Tap water - filled with contaminants like fluoride and chlorine
- Distilled water - the water is distilled (boiled) and the water vapours are collected in a different container. This type of water has no negative ions, nor positive ions so could be considered dead water
- Purified water – tap water which has been filtered, therefore it's free of contaminants
- Spring water – if it's not from a natural spring and it's in a plastic bottle then it is unstructured. Some plastic bottles contain xenoestrogen that causes hormonal imbalance by mimicking the effects of estrogen and promoting its production
- Ionized alkaline water – made from electrodes in water performing electrolysis to split the water molecule into positive hydrogen ions (H⁺) and negative hydroxide ions (OH⁻)

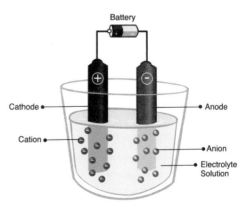

Figure 37
Water Electrolysis

101

Alkaline Water

The term 'alkaline' is somewhat misunderstood in our current society. It is often used as a way to indicate that something is healthy or good for you, when that is not what alkaline means. To understand this term you'll need to have a basic understanding of the pH scale. As previously mentioned, the term "pH" stands for potential of hydrogen or power of hydrogen, and it indicates the acidity level or alkalinity level of a water solution. The scale ranges from 0 to 14, with 7 being considered a neutral score. Anything below 7 is considered acidic and anything above 7 is considered alkaline. What's the significance of something being alkaline? Well, it all comes down to electrons. These are the subatomic particles orbiting atoms which carry a negative charge. The flow of electrons creates electricity, so the more electrons flowing throughout a water solution the greater the electric current. The reason why acids are looked at as the 'bad guys' and alkaline is considered 'good' is because acids have a tendency to steal electrons away from living things, whereas alkaline solutions tend to donate electrons to living things. This doesn't mean that all alkaline solutions are good for you, as one quick look online will show you that ammonia has a very high pH of 11 and bleach is even higher at 13. These two solutions are extremely alkaline, but I wouldn't recommend drinking them. The same logic can be applied to acids, not all acids are bad for you. Citrus fruits like lemons, limes and grapefruits are full of citric acid. However, they have all been shown to have a positive effect on health. Citric acid is so important to human health, that the main cycle involved in cellular respiration was named after it: The Citric Acid Cycle (later changed to Krebs Cycle). Acids are needed in order to accept electrons from alkaline solutions. This is actually the reason why you are made of acids. Think about it, your muscles are made of proteins and proteins are made up of amino acids. Your stomach is full of hydrochloric acid, a strong aqueous solution of hydrogen chloride that helps to breakdown the food you eat. The fat inside your body is made up of fatty acids and your genes are made up of DNA. What does DNA stand for? Deoxyribonucleic Acid. The building blocks of your genetic make-up are acids, so you are literally made of acids! Why? Because acids accept electrons, and your body is electric. It runs on electricity just like your smartphone does. Therefore, it needs to continue to accept electrons to keep running. I hope that makes sense. Try to remember this rule:

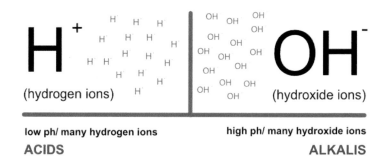

Figure 38
Acids & Alkali ions

102

Acids Accept Electrons
Alkaline Donate Electrons

If there are enough electrons to go around then the acids won't need to steal any electrons from living things. They will just accept what they've been given from the alkaline solution. If the electrons start to run out however, this is when the acids become dangerous as they may start stealing electrons from cells, tissues and organs, leading to what the science community call 'oxidation.' To avoid this we need alkaline water to donate electrons to acids. But not any type of alkaline water will do, as not all alkaline waters are good for you. The alkaline water needs to be structured in order for it to interact with your cells (see Figure 35). Does this mean that unstructured water is bad for you and should be avoided at all costs? Not in all cases. Take distilled water for example; this type of water is unstructured and has no electrical charge, so it could be considered 'dead water'. Charged ions in water move from a higher concentration to a lower concentration. So distilled water could pull electrons (and other particles) to it by simply being of a lower concentration. This could potentially be useful in teas or with herbs where you want the water to extract as much nutrients out of the herb as possible. But at the same time, if you drink 'dead water' on a regular basis it could start pulling electrons from your body; leaving your cells, tissues and organs electron deficient and mineral deficient. These are the direct consequences of drinking unstructured water regularly.

Unstructured Environments

Many of us live in environments where drinking unstructured water is inevitable due to the water that's available and accessible to us from the local supermarket (all the water on the shelves of supermarkets is unstructured). However, keep in mind that the unstructured water you drink can become structured internally. All it needs is sunlight energy (in the form of infrared light), heat and a hydrophilic surface. Internally, those hydrophilic surfaces are your cell membranes. Heat internally, is generated through movement and exercise, and sunlight energy is an external source available to all those who seek it. So your body has what it needs to structure water. The question then becomes, why doesn't your body do this all the time? In other words, why is your body not constantly structuring water? Here's where an analogy might work. I find that using simple analogies to illustrate complex scientific concepts can be quite useful at times and this same analogy was used in an earlier chapter to explain melanin's organising capabilities. Look at unstructured water like an untidy room. An untidy room stays untidy unless you tidy it up. The room doesn't tidy up itself; it requires your energy to do so. It's the same with unstructured water. It doesn't just structure itself; it requires you to do something to structure it. What can you do to structure your internal waters?

Exercise (creates the internal heat needed for structuring water)
Walk Barefoot on the Beach (electrons and infrared heat from the sand are absorbed through the feet)
Drink Green Vegetable Juice (living water = structured water)
Drink Coconut Water (straight from the coconut!)
Expose your skin to the sun (infrared radiation from the sun structures water)

Pseudoscience vs Common Sense

It's worth mentioning that structured water is actually considered 'pseudoscience' by a vast majority of the scientific community. What does the term pseudoscience mean? Online definitions describe pseudoscience as a collection of theories, assumptions, beliefs or methods mistakenly regarded as being scientific. Pseudoscience is often characterized by the following terms: contradictory, exaggerated, or unprovable. Simply put, any unsubstantiated claims inaccurately or even deceptively portrayed as science will be labelled 'pseudo.' Look up the term 'structured water' online and you'll find many articles claiming that it's fake and a scam. Apparently, there's 'no evidence' to support the claims made by Dr. Gerald Pollack about EZ water's health benefits. Therefore, the science community puts this label on it to stop people believing in it, I guess. So what should we believe? Is it fake or can the sun charge up water in a way that's beneficial for human health? Sometimes we just have to use common sense and go with our intuition over what the "experts" say. We live in a time where society wants you to abandon your own judgement, abandon your own logic and disregard all common sense. But just think for a moment, what makes more sense to you: Drinking green vegetable juice that has been naturally structured by sunlight and heat? Or drinking water from a plastic bottle, electrolysis machine or expensive filter? Science is simple. Why do we make it so complicated? Why do we continue to believe that 'science' needs to be proven in a laboratory setting, when nature is all the proof we need? Even if you don't believe in the term 'structured water' or 'EZ water', common sense should tell you that drinking the water from a plant is probably better for you than drinking the water from a pipe.

Structured Water Properties

Plant water, which is naturally structured by the sun, has a number of specific properties that make it different to any other type of water. The properties are listed below:

It has a high negative charge – In science, the term 'negative' is actually a good thing (and synonymous with alkaline). If something has a negative charge it means it has more electrons than protons. The flow of electrons creates an electrical current; this is the basis of electricity

It's an anti-oxidant with an abundance of electrons to donate – In science, oxidation is considered a bad thing, so anti-oxidants counteract the harmful effects of oxidation by donating electrons

It has an alkaline pH – Anything with a pH over 7 is considered alkaline. Not all alkaline fluids are good for you however (bleach is alkaline), but having an alkaline pH means that it has the ability to neutralise acids quickly

It's detoxifying – This is due to the exclusion zone excluding all toxins from it

It has tiny hexagonal molecular clusters (crystal lattice structure) – the molecules align themselves in a crystal lattice structure that resembles a hexagon (see Figure 32). What is the significance of this crystal lattice structure? Well, it is widely recognised that crystals can store data, so this type of structure may be able to store information

It can store energy & deliver energy like a battery – Due to having a positively charged end and a negatively charged end, the same as a battery (See Figure 33)

It hydrates the cells (passes easily through the cell membrane) – Water that doesn't go through the cell membrane usually goes straight through the body. This is why some people can drink litres of water and still be dehydrated, because that water is not actually penetrating the cells

It excludes impurities (exclusion zone) – even the smallest of particles are excluded

It's more viscous than ordinary water – more dense than H_2O

Once again for emphasis, this type of water is mainly built from sunlight and heat. You can't buy structured water from a shop, because there is a natural process to it. Knowing this will protect you from charlatans who may try to exploit this information by selling you 'structured water' in a bottle. The only real structured water we have access to is the water inside plants. Therefore, our best option for drinking structured water would be to extract the juice from water-rich fruits and vegetables. This type of water will be highly electric, full of vitamins and minerals, and natural sugars that the body needs for cellular energy. Caution may be necessary when juicing fruits, as it will be high in sugar. However, juicing dark green leafy vegetables will give your cells the structured water it needs without the high sugar content. Normal tap water or water out of a plastic bottle will not have the same effect. Why? Because this type of water is unstructured. According to Dr. Gerald Pollack, the water your cells require needs to be energised by the sun in order for the exclusion zone to build and extend around hydrophilic surfaces. The water inside the exclusion zone is negatively charged. The water just beyond the exclusion zone is positively charged, creating a liquid battery that can produce an electrical current (see Figure 33). Sunlight charges up this liquid battery. Thus, Dr. Pollack believes that water can receive and process energy drawn from the environment in much the same way as plants can through photosynthesis. He mentions in his book that absorbed light energy can then be exploited for performing work; including electrical and mechanical work, as well as the work of proteins inside cells.

Water Discoveries of the Past

Reading Dr. Pollack's book made me question a few things about science and water. I was curious as to why it seemed like he was the only scientist pioneering this type of water. Didn't anyone else figure this out before? Because as the old saying goes, "There is nothing new under the sun." So surely this knowledge of what water can do when it's structured had been discovered before? After doing some research I found quite quickly, that Dr. Pollack was not the first to discover the hidden wonders of water and that some scientists had in fact discovered the same properties many decades before. Most notably, Dr. Mona Harrison and Dr. Masaru Emoto. Both truly believed that water could be structured by our environment, creating hexagonal shapes that resemble a crystal lattice. Dr. Mona Harrison proved that our external environment had a direct effect on this crystal lattice structure, and Dr. Masaru Emoto believed that our internal environment (consisting of our thoughts and emotions) could actually affect it too. This didn't go down well with the scientific community. He was quickly labelled a pseudo-scientist when he started to claim that human consciousness could affect the molecular structure of water. Emoto used to perform experiments which involved exposing glasses of water to various words, pictures or music, then freezing the water and examining the frozen crystals under a microscope. He found that positive words and emotions, classical music and positive prayer directed at the water produced beautifully structured, colourful, snowflake-like patterns (see Figure 39). In contrast, he found that negative words and emotions, and music such as heavy metal, formed incomplete, asymmetrical patterns with dull colours. Despite becoming well-known for his experiments showing the effects of music, words and intentions on the structure of water, his work was never widely accepted as a credible source of information and his experiments were never published in a peer reviewed science journal. Nevertheless, Dr. Emoto's work continues to be very popular to this day, with millions of people sharing his online videos and buying his books.

Figure 39
Snowflake Pattern

Dr. Mona Harrison

Around the same time as Dr. Emoto was performing experiments in Japan to prove that human thoughts and intentions affect the molecular structure of water, there was another Doctor on the other side of the world doing her own experiments on water: The Honourable Dr. Mona Harrison. Who was the Honourable Dr. Mona Harrison? And what did she discover about water? Dr. Mona Harrison M.D. received her medical training at the University of Maryland, Harvard University and the Boston University Medical Center. She was the former assistant dean of the Boston University School of Medicine and former chief medical officer at the Washington, D.C. General Hospital. She specialized in homeopathy, paediatrics and nutrition, and had been the Director of the International Water Council before transitioning in 2003. Through her advanced studies in the field of quantum mechanics and the laws of cellular and biological regeneration of DNA, she discovered that the true value of structured water was its physical, psychical and spiritual properties, which according to her works were the keys to rejuvenation and longevity. She is often described as one of the master teachers who was sent here to spread the sacred knowledge of water; how a special kind of water can heal any disease, reverse aging and improve psychic functions and why having the best quality of water is critical to maintaining a healthy mind and body. During the 90's, she travelled the world sharing her breakthrough knowledge on how the right kind of water could rejuvenate humans on the cellular level and balance humans on a psychic level. This kind of water didn't really have a name at the time. In some very rare online recordings of Dr. Mona Harrison's lectures she describes this 'living water' as being "bioavailable" or being in a "bioavailable state." She explains that bioavailable water "gives something back to the cells" and allows the cells to heal. Other characteristics include the water having a crystalline shape and having very small molecular clusters. According to Dr. Harrison, all water clusters, including tap water; but it's the size of the clusters that makes the difference. She mentions that tap water is up at around 13-15 molecules per cluster. However, in bioavailable water it goes down to between 5-7 molecules per cluster. What is the significance of the smaller clusters with bioavailable water? It's all to do with cell permeability, or simply how water moves in and out of cells. The smaller the clusters, the easier it is for water to permeate or move into the cell. The larger the clusters, the more difficult it becomes to permeate the cell. Every cell in the human body requires water to function. If water cannot get into brain cells, for example, the brain cells will start to die. This is something Dr. Mona Harrison emphasized in her lectures. She talked about the blood-brain barrier and how only the tiniest of clusters can permeate this barrier. According to her research, it is the bioavailable water that goes straight into the brain, allowing the brain to get the 90% water it requires to function optimally.

Bioavailable Water Characteristics

Another very important characteristic of bioavailable water is that it has a negative oxidation-reduction potential. In science, the term oxidation refers to a loss of electrons, whilst the term reduction refers to a gain of electrons. Remember, electricity is the flow of electrons. So any water solution that can conduct electricity will have an oxidation-reduction potential, which can be measured in millivolts (mV). A positive potential would lead to a more oxidising water solution, whereas a negative potential signifies a reducing water solution with an abundance of electrons. Dr. Harrison demonstrated that bioavailable water had a negative oxidation-reduction potential, and therefore carried a negative electrical charge. The net charge Dr. Harrison observed whilst studying this type of water was -200 mV. This is similar to what Dr. Gerald Pollack had observed about structured water. He mentions in his book that EZ water is negatively charged with a negative potential of between -120 mV and -200 mV. The similarities between their works are uncanny. For example, Dr. Pollack has noted that EZ water builds around what he calls "hydrophilic surfaces." These hydrophilic surfaces create the exclusion zone by separating the hydrogen and oxygen. This is eerily similar to what Dr. Harrison has described as electrolysis membranes. She noted that the body is filled with electrolysis membranes. These membranes facilitate the splitting of water into hydrogen and oxygen just like the hydrophilic surfaces Dr. Pollack describes. It doesn't take a genius to realise that these two great scientific minds are describing the same phenomena. Dr. Harrison believed that electrolysis water machines, which mimic structured water by splitting the water molecule into hydrogen and oxygen, are just trying to replicate nature. They are just replicating what your body does internally with water under the right conditions.

Bioavailable water is structured, and structured water is bioavailable. Hydrophilic surfaces perform electrolysis and electrolysis membranes are hydrophilic. It's not rocket science; we are talking about the same thing here. This is why decoding scientific language is so important, because terminology and nomenclature in science tend to change over time. However, the way nature works and thus the way the body works is a universal truth, it never changes. And all we need to do to tap into this universal truth is to look within. The universe is not just outside of you. It is within you as well. This is where the science of self truly dwells; where all the answers to life's mysteries can be found. It is very challenging to accept this reality when modern science is used as a weapon of mass confusion, a mind manipulation tool used to sway you to believe one thing over another. Science has become the new religion. Just like religion, people in the science community can sometimes hold very strong beliefs where nothing you say can change what they believe to be true. And just like religion, what I've found through my own observations is that, when you start to peel back the layers and look at the principles underlying these belief systems, you'll find more similarities than differences. Dr. Mona Harrison, Dr. Masaru Emoto and Dr. Gerald Pollack all convey the same principles when it comes to the water we should be drinking. It should be alkaline, bioavailable, negatively charged and structured by our environment.

1 What is the best water for melanin?
  A. Tap Water
  B. Distilled Water
  C. Ionized Alkaline Water
  D. Structured (EZ) Water

2 What is structured (EZ) water?
  A. A natural type of water where the H_2O molecule splits into positively charged ions (H^+) and negatively charged ions (OH^-) creating a liquid battery
  B. Boiled water where the water vapours have been collected in a different container
  C. The type of water made from electrodes performing electrolysis to split the water molecule into positive ions (H^+) and negative ions (OH^-)
  D. The bottled water that you can buy from your local supermarket

3 According to Dr. Gerald Pollack, what builds EZ water in your cells?
  A. Sunlight (infrared light from the sun)
  B. Green Juicing (drinking the 'living water' from green plants)
  C. Earthing (walking barefoot on the Earth)
  D. All the above

4 What is the chemical formula of EZ water?
  A. H_2O
  B. H_3O_2
  C. H_2O_2
  D. H_3O

5 Which of the following is not one of the specific properties of structured water?
  A. It has a negative charge
  B. It has an alkaline pH
  C. It protects against the 'harmful' effects of UV radiation
  D. It excludes impurities (exclusion zone)

6 **If you were to look at structured water under a microscope what sort of structure are you likely to see?**
   A.   3-D Tetrahedral Structure
   B.   Hexagonal Crystalline Lattice Structure
   C.   Ancient Kemetic Pyramid Structure
   D.   No structure at all. It's all pseudoscience!

7 **According to Dr. Masaru Emoto, what else other than sunlight and heat can structure water?**
   A.   Positive Thoughts and Intentions
   B.   Loving Words and Emotions
   C.   Classical Music
   D.   All the above

8 **What was the term that Dr. Mona Harrison used to describe structured water's state?**
   A.   Bioavailable State
   B.   Unavailable State
   C.   Semi-available State
   D.   All the above

CHAPTER EIGHT

MELANIN CONFUSION

MELANIN CONFUSION

When it comes to learning science there tends to be a lot of scientific jargon used when explaining simple topics. The scientific jargon is usually big words, medical terminology, hidden meanings, or quite frankly waffle. It seems to be used specifically to keep lay people out of the know, out of the circle so to speak. Latin nomenclature is a classic example of this. During the Roman Empire reign, Latin was established as the lingua franca of religion and knowledge. Everything that was worth knowing – from science, to law, to medicine– was written down in Latin. If you wanted to be someone in the Empire, you needed to speak, read and write the language. Unfortunately this out-dated ideology still persists today.

It's because of this very reason that I believe many of us do not like science. We find it confusing, complex, baffling or just boring. The terminology used in science is such a totally different language to the lay person that they switch off, and stop concentrating on what's being said; the same way you'd switch off if you were around two electricians speaking about electrical wiring and you didn't know a thing about electricity. But what if you did? What if you knew the jargon and could understand what the electricians were saying clearly and precisely? All of a sudden the confusion is gone and you can appreciate the conversation (and maybe even partake in it). This makes decoding the language very important.

In the next chapter, I will decode the common types of confusing language that scientists use around melanin. This will bring much clarity to a subject that, if we're being honest, everyone should know about. Because remember, **everyone** has melanin. You can't be a living, breathing, fully functional human being without it. So understanding **The Hidden Science of Melanin** is valuable knowledge for all of us, whether you're conscious of this fact or not. Now as stated earlier, I do not blame the scientists for using confusing language to describe melanin. They are just regurgitating what they were taught during their educational process. However, the great poet and scholar Maya Angelou once said "Do the best you can until you know better. Then when you know better, do better." Hopefully this book can be one of the tools that scientists, doctors, teachers, lecturers and educators use to "do better" when it comes to how they talk about melanin. Use this book to change the narrative, to ensure that our children do not grow up to be as confused as we were about melanin when we were their age. It should be our duty of care to ensure that the next generation are given the right information about how their body works and the role that melanin plays in all biological systems. Why would you not want your children to know the truth? That's a question I'd like every naysayer of this book to answer (and there will be naysayers), because I have found through my own observation that confused children often grow up to become confused adults.

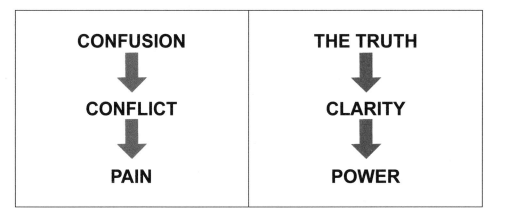

Please take a look at the confusion flow chart diagram and commit it to memory!! I start every single one of my university lectures with this diagram. Copy the diagram on paper repeatedly. This will help you memorise it in an easy manner. Never forget what confusion leads to. Confusion **always** (emphasis on always) leads to conflict. That conflict could be between people (misinterpretations, disputes, arguments, fights, wars) or could be internal within the individuals own mind (mental conflict, psychological issues, cognitive dissonance). Conflict leads to pain. And pain is not always felt physically. That pain could be physical, mental, emotional, psychological, social or spiritual. In order to resolve the pain caused by confusion we need an antidote. What is the universal antidote for confusion? The Truth! Truth leads to clarity and clarity is power! So let's start empowering our children with the right knowledge and information from as early as possible. And what better way to start the empowerment process than to explain to them what they see when they look in the mirror? All children have melanin, so why aren't the different types of melanin taught in schools? I find the omission of melanin from the English educational system quite astonishing, to say the least. Even when children are taught about melanin they seem to be only taught one aspect of it.

Confusing Children About Melanin

Go onto any educational website aimed at children and read how they explain melanin. Look in any biology book aimed at children and read the section on skin. You're going to notice a pattern, a similarity in how they all describe melanin's characteristics. What is that similarity? You'll find they all describe melanin in terms of its protective properties. You've probably already noticed this pattern before. Every time you read up about melanin the main function everyone likes to point out is the fact that it protects you from the harmful effects of UV radiation. This is true; melanin does protect your DNA from UV radiation damage. But is that its only function? Heck, is that even its main function? Think about all of the amazing things you've learnt about melanin from reading this book so far.

- Melanin is a refined, complex, **multifunctional** chemical that has a wide variety of important functions within the human body, and in the environment (Professor Carol Barnes)

- Melanin has a broad absorption spectrum (Dr. Karl Maret)

- Absorbs thousands of times more electromagnetic radiation than chlorophyll (Dr. Karl Maret)

- Melanin can see light, hear sound and smell scents (Nadine L. Wicks et al., Alireza Bina, Lian Gelis et al.)

- Melanin is strategically located in areas of the body where energy conversion or charge transfer occurs (Dr. T. Owens Moore)

- Melanin can convert light energy to sound energy (music) and back again to light energy (Dr. Frank Barr et al.)

- Melanin is centrally involved in controlling all mental and physical body capabilities (Dr. Frank Barr et al.)

- It helps to prevent DNA damage in cells (Dr. T. Owens Moore)

- Found throughout the entire body of all humans in their skin, eyes, endocrine glands, blood, heart, muscles, lungs, gastrointestinal tract, kidney/urogenital tract, sexual organs and the brain (Dr Richard King)

- Found in almost every organ of the body and is necessary for the brain and nerves to operate, the eyes to see and the cells to reproduce (Dr. T. Owens Moore)

- Melanin transduces both acoustic and electric energy fields and it can generate enough heat to effect metabolic processes (Dr. Frank Barr et al.)

- Melanin in the iris of the eye is directly related to an individual's reaction time or quickness of movement (E. J. Lerner)

- Melanin can dissociate (split) the water molecule into hydrogen and oxygen, like chlorophyll does in plants (Dr Auturo Solis Herrera)

- Melanin is critical to hearing (Dr Richard King)

- Sound needs melanin to be heard (M. Tachibana)

- Melanin is an important energy regulating molecule in the body (Dr Karl Maret)

- Is present in developing foetus (Dr Karl Maret)

- Thought to be a master molecule for steering biological processes in the body (Dr Karl Maret)

Despite all of the evidence revealing that melanin is multifunctional; despite academic published papers scientifically proving that melanin is involved in embryogenesis, energy conversion, light and sound transduction, and sexual reproduction; despite research showing that melanin is in many tissues, not just the skin. Despite all of this, the main thing children are taught about melanin is that it protects them from that huge bright star in the sky that gives life to every living thing we see on this planet. The logic makes no sense. Sometimes analogies work best when trying to explain logic, so visualise this analogy if you can: Imagine if your child asked you why they had a digestive system. What would you say to them?

"Mummy, Daddy.. Why do I have a digestive system?"

What's your response? Would your response be,

"Oh, you have a digestive system to protect you from the harmful effects of food."

Notice how silly that sounds. Now, just to be clear, your digestive system does protect you from the harmful effects of food. However, would you say that protection is its main function? Would this be the only thing you'd tell your children about their digestive system? Probably not. Chances are you'd say more than that. Perhaps you might say, "You have a digestive system so you can breakdown and digest the food you eat. Your digestive system assimilates the nutrients from food and converts it into energy. Your body can then utilise this energy to live." So how should we explain what melanin does to children? Use the same simple language. "You have melanin so you can absorb sunlight (digest sunlight, so to speak). Your melanin assimilates sunlight and converts it into energy. Your body can then utilise this energy to live." Going back to the digestive system analogy, if you wanted to explain to children the "protective properties" of digestion you might say that the nutrients which are not utilised by the body after digestion get excreted as waste. The waste, if left in the body, could become harmful to your biological systems. In other words, the protective function is an afterthought. It's the same with melanin. Yes, melanin protects our DNA from ultraviolet radiation, but this is not the main reason we all have melanin. The main reason we all have melanin is for energy conversion.

It's very simple, but for some reason many professionals who know what melanin does still choose to emphasise its protective properties over everything else. Can you imagine if every child in school was only taught about the protective properties of their digestive system? What would their classes be like?

"Hello class,

Today you are going to learn about the digestive system and here goes...

It protects you from harmful fruits. The end!"

I am not trying to be humorous here; I am just trying to illustrate my point. Think about how children would start to view fruits if all they were taught about fruits was that they were "harmful" and "high in sugar." And that the only reason why they have a digestive system is to protect them from the deadly apples, mangoes, grapes and bananas they eat. They might start viewing all fruits as dangerous, instead of as nutritious. This could lead to them avoiding fruits altogether, resulting in nutritional deficiencies, stunted growth and development, and eating disorders. Think about the knock-on effect that would have on their health as they grow into adulthood. This is exactly the erroneous approach used when explaining to children what melanin does. The focus is always on the 'harmful' effects of sunlight.

Sunlight Confusion

"Melanin protects you from the harmful effects of UV radiation." I can't tell you how many times I've heard an 'expert' say that as a response to the question "What does melanin do?" If children are constantly told that the sun is this dangerous thing which emits these super harmful rays that damage their skin, what sort of knock-on effect might that have? The sun gives life to every living organism on this Earth. This includes plant organisms, animal organisms and human organisms. It excludes none. Life would cease to exist without sunlight. All aspects of sunlight—from infrared, to visible, to ultraviolet radiation—are essential for human life. Vitamin D needs UVB radiation to be synthesised in the skin. Nitric Oxide is made in the skin when your melanin is exposed to UVA. Nitric Oxide vasodilates your blood vessels which improves blood circulation all over your body. These are just some of the physiological benefits of UV radiation on the human body that children should know about. Why? Because the truth is the only antidote to confusion. Let's start teaching children the truth about themselves so they grow up to really appreciate who they are and how their body works. Melanin doesn't block sunlight, it absorbs it. This error of thinking needs to be eradicated if we honestly want children to know the truth. If melanin blocked sunlight all dark-skinned people would have rickets, due to the body not being able to process vitamin D. Dark skinned people in general would have weak bones as we are told the main thing that vitamin D helps with is the absorption of calcium from the gut. The Maasai people of Kenya proves this to be false! Watch this tribe perform their traditional Maasai jumping dance, Adamu (or Adumu) and tell me they've got weak bones.

Sun Block Confusion

Melanin blocks sunlight? Sport proves this to be false! Look at what Michael Jordan did during his prime playing for the Chicago Bulls, or look at what Usain Bolt did in the Beijing Olympics. Michael Jordan used to jump from the free throw line to dunk the basketball. Am I supposed to believe that his melanin blocked sunlight? How on Earth was he able to do that with weak knees? Wheaties?! Do you know how much pressure is placed on your whole skeletal system from running and jumping? Usain Bolt had the world in absolute awe at how fast he could run. Where do you think he was getting all that energy from? Chicken nuggets?! Melanin doesn't block sunlight, stop the lies! It absorbs it. And that absorption charges up your melanin like a battery.

Blocking the sun is not a natural thing and therefore doesn't truly exist in nature. The chlorophyll in green leaves, the soil in the Earth, the sand that makes up the beach and even the water that makes up the sea, all absorb different frequencies of sunlight. Anything that blocks the sun is unnatural. However, due to the 'apparent' threat of global warming and the supposed 'risks' of climate change some believe that blocking out the sun, or at least dimming it to some degree, is a good idea. In 2021, experts from Harvard University began working on a project to spray millions of tonnes of chalk into the stratosphere, in an attempt to 'dim the sun' and cool the Earth [74].

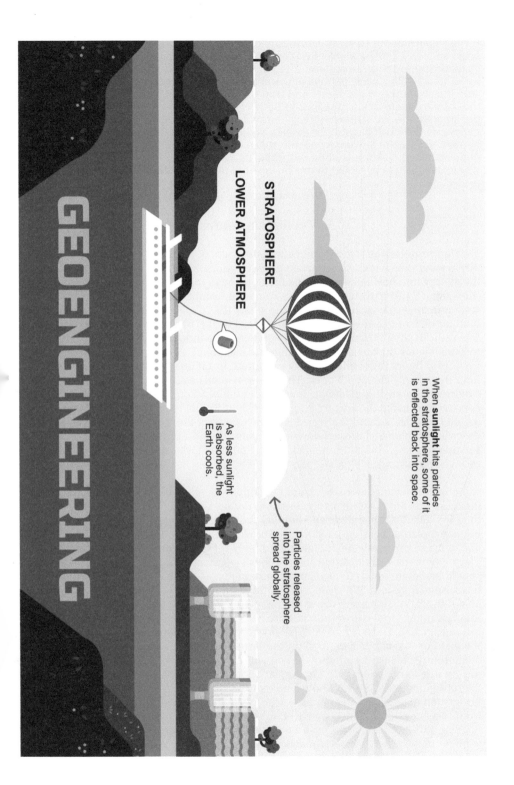

GEOENGINEERING

STRATOSPHERE

LOWER ATMOSPHERE

When **sunlight** hits particles in the stratosphere, some of it is reflected back into space.

Particles released into the stratosphere spread globally.

As less sunlight is absorbed, the Earth cools.

It was reported that Harvard University experts will test the system by sending a large balloon 12 miles above the Swedish town of Kiruna and have it drop 2kg of chalk dust into the stratosphere. The aim of the estimated $3 million mission, backed by billionaire Bill Gates, is to have the chalk deflect a portion of the sun's radiation, stop it from hitting the surface, and cool the planet (see Figure 40). If all goes to plan, the Harvard team will be the first in the world to move solar geoengineering out of the lab and into the stratosphere. Will this be a great thing for the planet? What will happen to the plant kingdom if the sun is dimmed or blocked completely? What will happen to the people whose melanin relies on sunlight for energy? Contrary to popular belief, melanin is not a natural sunscreen, as it literally does the opposite of what sunscreen is designed to do. However, it does play an important role in protection.

Protection Confusion

Melanin protects you from the harmful effects of UV radiation by absorbing and **dissipating** this energy so it doesn't damage your DNA. It does this by transforming the energy into harmless amounts of heat through a process called "ultrafast internal conversion". Internal conversion is a transition from a higher to a lower electronic state in a molecule or atom [75]. Melanin has the "ultrafast" ability to dissipate more than >99.9% of the absorbed UV radiation as heat [76] and keep the generation of free radicals at a minimum [77]. This prevents the indirect DNA damage which is responsible for the formation of malignant melanoma. So melanin does protect your DNA from the harmful effects of UV radiation. But it doesn't block sunlight, as many have mistakenly claimed before. Therefore, it is misleading to call melanin a "natural sunscreen" or anything similar. If we want children to truly understand melanin we need to start using the correct language when describing its functions. From this day on, all scientists around the world should stop using the word "block" when describing melanin's interaction with the sun. Melanin protects you from UV radiation by absorbing it, not blocking it. And the more exposure to UV radiation it receives the stronger the absorption rate [78].

Although protecting your DNA from UV damage is obviously a very important function, it is not melanin's only function. It does so much more than that. Isn't it time we start teaching children about all the other functions of melanin as well? And not just melanin, because as you now know from reading this book, melanin is just one of many pigments inside the human body that play vital roles in our biology. These pigments work together like a cohesive system with a common goal. Children should be taught about their pigment system just as much as they're taught about their skeletal system. Why? Because nothing happens in your body without pigments absorbing light. Just think about the pigment chlorophyll. Chlorophyll's role in plants is very similar to melanin's role in humans. Chlorophyll absorbs sunlight and utilises this energy to perform a series of chemical reactions inside the plant that results in the plant producing its own food (in the form of glucose). This is photosynthesis. Now if chlorophyll blocked sunlight what do you think would happen to the plant? It would die out due to not being able to perform photosynthesis. Plants, algae, and even some microorganisms all rely on photosynthesis to live. In other words, they all rely on the absorption of sunlight energy and water to stay alive. Anything that blocks the plant from receiving sunlight or water would lead to the death of the plant. This is not my opinion, this is science. Matter of fact, this is universal law. Plants need water and sunlight to live. Now, here's a question for you to ponder: What would happen to the plant if you covered it with sunscreen? I'll let you put two and two together on that one.

118

Skin Confusion

Being a student and a teacher of science for over 15 years, I've noticed that skin seems to be a taboo subject to talk about. Not just in regards to children, but with adults as well. There always seems to be a reluctance to speak openly and honestly about skin; and skin colour to be more specific. Why do you think this is? We are constantly being taught that we are all one race, the human race; and that the differences between us are so minuscule that it's not worth pointing them out. I find this narrative very interesting. You don't hear people saying that about animals, do you? Animals are all part of one kingdom, the animal kingdom. That doesn't negate the fact that animals are different. A lion is different from a tiger. They are very similar, but different. Their differences should be explored so that children do not grow up confused about lions and tigers. Children learning the differences between lions and tigers would not cause the children to feel any animosity to one or the other. Logically speaking, they would just appreciate the differences. It's exactly the same with humans. Our differences should be explored, studied, evaluated and appreciated so that children do not grow up confused about the different types of melanin in humans. Children are taught about all the different types of animals in the animal kingdom, and rightfully so. Natural Historians like Sir David Attenborough have made a career out of teaching us, through various nature documentaries, the differences in animals and plants; in how they behave, eat, look and live. We are all fascinated watching these documentaries about the biological differences of the most amazing natural creatures and plants of this planet. The different colour of flowers and leaves always tells us something unique about the biochemical nature of the plant and its environment. We are left with a better understanding of the plants around us after being taught these valuable lessons at school or after watching nature documentaries. But for some strange reason, if we put the exact same focus into learning about the biological differences in humans all of a sudden everyone gets tight lipped and nervous. Children should know what type of melanin they have just as much as they should know the blood type they carry; whether it's A, B, AB or O. This information is not only important for the child to understand him or herself better, it's also important for medical reasons.

Carbon Confusion

Every science class that children take at school, especially biology and chemistry, should cover melanin in detail. Biology is the scientific study of living organisms. How can one study living organisms without studying the main pigment present in all living organisms? Eumelanin. Chemistry is the scientific study of the properties and behaviour of matter. It's a natural science that covers the elements that make up matter like Oxygen, Hydrogen, Nitrogen and Carbon. How can anyone study carbon without studying melanin? Carbon is the main element found in melanin. If you were to breakdown melanin into its original elements you'll find that it's made up of Carbon, Hydrogen, Nitrogen and Oxygen. The chemical formula is $C_{18} H_{10} N_2 O_4$. Try not to get confused by the numbers. Just note that the higher the number the more of that element is present in the chemical. So melanin is more carbon than it is anything else. This might aid in one's understanding of the relationship between melanin and carbon. It was once said that "There's no such thing as melanin, its carbon!" This quote is from the great Dr. Sebi and it has been repeated many times by those who follow his teachings. Here's a transcript from a popular video online where Dr. Sebi talks about melanin and carbon.

"Interviewer: "Umm...What is melanin and what is carbon? Tell us about those two [minerals], or whatever they are?

Dr. Sebi: "Melanin is not a mineral! Melanin is a word that was used to describe a certain biological function. But that particular identification, or category, or thing, melanin, is a European identification of what they think activates those neurons in our body that makes us black. But, when you break down our body, our biological structure into what we would have to put it in, which is chemistry, biochemistry... melanin has no place. It's not to be found. What is found in the body, that is attributed to melanin, is carbon! Carbon not only determines the quality of life in black folks. Carbon determines the quality of life in every living plant that exists that is natural. If carbon is absent, there's no life! Melanin, what is it? I don't know."

Dr. Sebi is someone who I'd consider to be one of the master teachers when it comes to health and biochemistry. So to hear him say this I really had to analyse what he was saying. The key part of what he said that truly gave me clarity about melanin is where he says, *"What is found in the body, that is attributed to melanin, is carbon!"* I find this to be a true statement because the main thing most people attribute to melanin in humans is blackness. That blackness must come from carbon. According to who? Leon Marshall? No, according to logic. Remember, melanin is not a mineral, nor is it an element. So, it doesn't appear on the periodic table of elements that lists all elements known to man. It is however, listed as a chemical, with the chemical formula of $C_{18} H_{10} N_2 O_4$. Now, just pause for a second and take a look at this formula. The C stands for Carbon, the H stands for Hydrogen, the N is for Nitrogen and the O is for Oxygen. Out of these 4 elements, which one is the main element that is attributed to melanin? Obviously it's carbon! Because hydrogen is a gas which wouldn't explain the blackness of melanin, nitrogen is a colourless, odorless and mostly inert gas, which wouldn't explain the blackness or the rhythmic movement of melanin. Same with oxygen. These are all colourless gases. So the blackness or physical appearance of melanin must come from carbon. It cannot come from any other element in that chemical formula, logically speaking.

So let's be clear, Dr. Sebi is totally correct where this is concerned. He is also 100% correct when he says *"Carbon not only determines the quality of life in black folks. Carbon determines the quality of life in every living plant that exists that is natural. If carbon is absent, there's no life!"* This is very true as carbon is key to the body's ability to form polymers (the binding of elements and molecules to create long chains or units). The science community call melanin a biopolymer due to its long carbon chains. Carbon has an atomic number of 6. Meaning a carbon atom has 6 protons, 6 neutrons, and 6 electrons. Due to its unique structure, a carbon atom can bond with four other atoms. This feature makes carbon the universal element binder. Elements (Atoms) need to bind together to form molecules, molecules bind together to form compounds. And compounds are needed by the body for various reasons. For example, a carbohydrate is a compound formed by the binding of three main elements: Carbon, Hydrogen and Oxygen. We should all be familiar with carbohydrates as we eat them on a daily basis. Side note: real carbohydrates come from plants! Any other type of carbohydrate is processed and unnatural leading to the common diseases and illnesses we see in today's society. The best types of carbohydrates for melanin are covered in the *FOODS FOR MELANIN* chapter. Feel free to go back and re-read that chapter to fully appreciate what types of carbohydrates we should be consuming.

According to Dr. Sebi, Carbon, Hydrogen and Oxygen are the main 'players' of life. He once said, "Without these three players, ...there could be no life expression." We must keep in mind that Hydrogen and Oxygen are gases. They are intangible, meaning you can't touch these gases by themselves. Now here's what makes Carbon so important to all living organisms on Earth. When you add carbon to these two intangible gases you get something tangible. Once you introduce carbon into the mix, you create the millions and billions of tangible matter that exist in nature. I was made aware of this by a melanin scholar named Minister Enqi. In many of his online teachings, he explains that the magic of carbon is its ability to turn the invisible into the visible. Carbon binds with hydrogen and oxygen to make an apple, a grapefruit, a mango, or a watermelon. In other words, something you can touch and eat. This is the magic of carbon; it is the universal element binder. It can take something that is intangible (like hydrogen and oxygen) and make it tangible (like a fruit). It can take something that is unseen and make it seen. Another scholar that I consider a master teacher is Professor Kaba Hiawatha Kamene. He has a book by the name of *Spirituality Before Religions: Spirituality is Unseen Science...Science is Seen Spirituality*. The way I've heard him explain carbon is perfect. He calls carbon the "cosmic glue." He says "It is the evidence of everything in all that exists." It has the ability to link atoms together cohesively. No other element on the periodic table can do this. When it links atoms together it often forms hexagonal shapes that are evident everywhere in nature. Even throughout this book you might've noticed all the hexagonal shapes that keep appearing. Have you noticed them? The aromatic amino acids, the structured water, the molecular structure of melatonin, dopamine and tyrosine. These hexagons do not appear coincidently. They are due to the magic of carbon, the cosmic glue that holds everything we see in nature together. When carbon creates these hexagons it gives that molecule the magical ability to capture photons. So anytime you see a molecular structure with the six-sided carbon ring, this means it can partake in light energy absorption. Not all molecules on Earth have this privilege, hence the reason why the hexagonal shape is considered to be esoteric and symbolises Sacred Geometry. In most ancient practises light is synonymous with knowledge, so being able to absorb a broad spectrum of light is considered DIVINE. With that being said, take one look at the molecular structure in Figure 41. This is MELANIN. Look at how many carbon rings are part of its molecular structure. Carbon creates molecules that can ingest light. And if we're being scientifically honest, life would cease to exist on Earth without light. So Dr. Sebi was right!

However, we need to understand why he said what he said and not just take it at face value. Because if we take Dr. Sebi's words on just face value we could then say that there's no such thing as a protein, its carbon! Some might agree with this statement, considering the other three elements that make up a protein are gases (hydrogen, nitrogen and oxygen). However, the point I am trying to make is that the cosmic glue of carbon binds different elements together to form all the different molecules we see in nature. That means everything could be called carbon. Take coal for example, the abundant natural resource which is used as a fuel to generate electric power. Coal is made of carbon. If we take Dr. Sebi's words on just face value we could say that

Melanin Full Structure

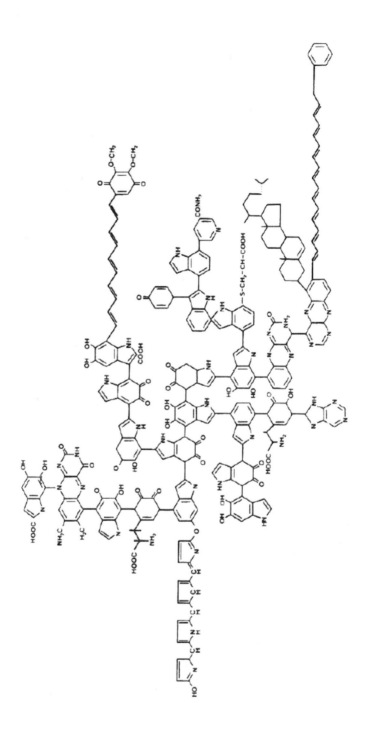

Figure 41

there's no such thing as coal, "its carbon." Coal is carbon, so we wouldn't be wrong in saying that. But do you see where I'm going with this? It is well believed that diamonds are a girl's best friend. Well, what are diamonds made of? Carbon. If we take the master teacher's words on just face value we could say that there's no such thing as diamonds, "its carbon!" So should we change the popular phrase to "carbon is a girl's best friend"? I am not trying to be facetious; I am just trying to illustrate my point. All living things on Earth are composed of carbon. It is the main component of sugars, fats, proteins, muscle tissue, DNA, hair and of course skin. I am very conscious not to say that the master teacher Dr. Sebi was wrong about melanin, because technically he wasn't. I can totally understand why he said "its carbon." Hopefully after reading this, you can too.

> "Black was the color of carbon, the key atom found in all living matter. Carbon atoms link together to form black melanin, the first chemical that could capture light and reproduce itself." –Dr. Richard King (African Origin of Biological Psychiatry)"

Dark Universe Confusion

Have you ever noticed how the words black and dark are used in science? Especially the word 'dark'. This word is often used in science when describing the composition of the universe. According to NASA, 68 percent of the universe is dark energy, 27 percent is dark matter and 5 percent is what they call normal matter [79]. This normal matter is everything that we can physically touch, see, feel and taste here on planet Earth. That's a very small percentage of what makes up the universe, don't you think? If NASA is correct in their estimations of what the universe is composed of, then essentially the universe is just darkness. Or is it? As previously mentioned, to truly understand science you need to break down the language. So, let's start breaking down the language used to describe the universe. What is dark energy? Here is an excerpt from an article published on the official NASA website entitled: Dark Energy, Dark Matter

> In the early 1990s, one thing was fairly certain about the expansion of the universe. It might have enough energy density to stop its expansion and recollapse, it might have so little energy density that it would never stop expanding, but gravity was certain to slow the expansion as time went on. Granted, the slowing had not been observed, but, theoretically, the universe had to slow. The universe is full of matter and the attractive force of gravity pulls all matter together. Then came 1998 and the Hubble Space Telescope (HST) observations of very distant supernovae that showed that, a long time ago, the universe was actually expanding more slowly than it is today. So the expansion of the universe has not been slowing due to gravity, as everyone thought, it has been accelerating. No one expected this, no one knew how to explain it. But something was causing it.

Eventually theorists came up with three sorts of explanations. Maybe it was a result of a long-discarded version of Einstein's theory of gravity, one that contained what was called a "cosmological constant." Maybe there was some strange kind of energy-fluid that filled space. Maybe there is something wrong with Einstein's theory of gravity and a new theory could include some kind of field that creates this cosmic acceleration. Theorists still don't know what the correct explanation is, but they have given the solution a name. It is called dark energy.

What Is Dark Energy?

More is unknown than is known. We know how much dark energy there is because we know how it affects the universe's expansion. Other than that, it is a complete mystery. But it is an important mystery. It turns out that roughly 68% of the universe is dark energy. Dark matter makes up about 27%. The rest - everything on Earth, everything ever observed with all of our instruments, all normal matter - adds up to less than 5% of the universe. Come to think of it, maybe it shouldn't be called "normal" matter at all, since it is such a small fraction of the universe.

After reading that you should now have a better understanding on what dark energy is, right? Nah me neither! And this is my issue with scientific language; so much is written, but in a very unclear incomprehensive way. Science should be used to help you better understand this universe, not make you even more confused about it. According to NASA, dark energy is a "complete mystery" apparently. So to this day, despite the amazing intelligent minds that have walked this planet Earth over the course of a millennia, despite the genius contributions from the likes of Albert Einstein and Sir Isaac Newton, despite NASA having ventured into this dark mysterious energy to get to the Moon (right?), we are still no closer to understanding what dark energy is. What about dark matter? Are NASA able to clearly express what this is? Here's how they explain dark matter:

We are much more certain what dark matter is not than we are what it is. First, it is dark, meaning that it is not in the form of stars and planets that we see. Observations show that there is far too little visible matter in the universe to make up the 27% required by the observations. Second, it is not in the form of dark clouds of normal matter, matter made up of particles called baryons. We know this because we would be able to detect baryonic clouds by their absorption of radiation passing through them. Third, dark matter is not antimatter, because we do not see the unique gamma rays that are produced when antimatter annihilates with matter. Finally, we can rule out large galaxy-sized black holes on the basis of how many gravitational lenses we see. High concentrations of matter bend light passing near them from objects further away, but we do not see enough lensing events to suggest that such objects to make up the required 25% dark matter contribution.

Once again, a lengthy response but not much clarity there. They know what dark matter is not, but they don't know what it is. So dark matter, just like dark energy, is also one complete mystery to the scientists working over at NASA. Isn't that interesting? These are the same NASA scientists who apparently were smart enough to build a spacecraft that took humans into this unknown dark territory and safely landed them on the Moon way back in 1969.

If you don't know what this dark mysterious matter is, how are you able to build a spacecraft capable of flying through it? And why haven't you been back? These are just logical questions that I believe someone using common sense would ask. In fact, these questions have already been posed to the scientists and astronauts of NASA about the famous spaceflight that first landed humans on the Moon. According to one of NASA's oldest active astronauts Donald Petitt, the reason why NASA has never been back to the moon since 1969 is because they destroyed the technology that they used to get there in the first place, and for some strange reason can't build it back again. No seriously, he actually said this when asked the obvious question of why NASA hadn't been back to the Moon. Here's the full quote of what he said...

"I'd go to the Moon in a nanosecond. The problem is we don't have the technology to do that anymore. We used to but we destroyed that technology and it's a painful process to build it back again." -Don Petitt

I'm confused. Why would NASA destroy the technology they used to go to the moon? These are the scientists and experts we rely on to tell us what we need to know about this beautiful universe we live in. Hopefully now you can fully understand why so many of us are confused when it comes to science. We are constantly receiving information from experts that just doesn't add up. We are taught science in a way that makes no logical sense at all. How are we supposed to make sense of this dark universe we live in if we are all confused about science? Even using the word "dark" to describe the universe doesn't make sense. Think about what that word really means. According to most definitions it means having very little or no light. Look up the word "darkness" and you'll see it's defined as "the absence of light." How can that explain the universe considering all the stars that shine bright up there? One of those stars is important to the way we live here on Earth. That star is made up of Hydrogen and Helium and gives life to all living organisms on this planet. That star is the SUN and it is the focal point of our solar system. So there is immense light in the universe, there's no way the universe is 'absent of light.' Using the word 'dark' is inaccurate to describe the universe considering the intense radiation (light = radiation) that is beyond the Earth's atmosphere. The radiation is so intense that to this day some astronauts still believe it's impossible for humans to survive going through the Van Allen belts without adequate protection from these rays. The Van Allen belts, named after James Van Allen, the physicist who discovered them in 1958, make up the inner region of the Earth's magnetic field and can swell when the sun becomes more active. In other words, the sun can cause these belts to emit even more radiation (radiation = light) and therefore become even more dangerous to human exposure. According to logic and evidence, the universe is filled with intense radiation and immense light. Thus, using the word dark to describe the universe is very inaccurate. So what word would be a better, more accurate way to describe the universe? Black!

How We See Black Colour

White Light

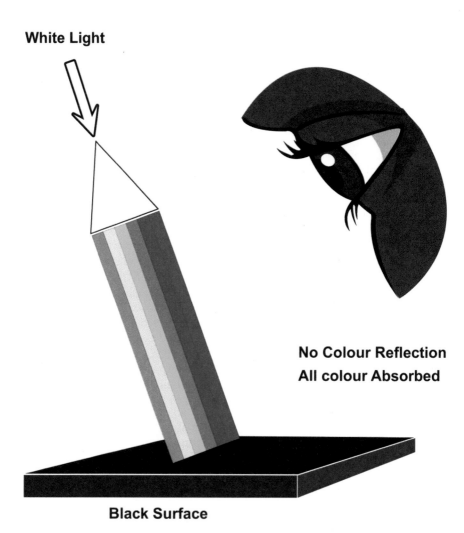

No Colour Reflection

All colour Absorbed

Black Surface

Figure 42
How We See Black

Black Light Confusion

Light that is invisible to the human eye is scientifically considered black light. So any light that falls outside of the visible spectrum on the electromagnetic spectrum is black. According to who, Leon Marshall? No, according to science. Anytime I'm teaching science I always like to tell people not to believe a word I say. Instead, I encourage them to pick up their smartphone and make their phone smart. According to dictionary.com black light is "ultraviolet or infrared radiation, invisible to the eye." In other words, any light frequencies that fall outside of the visible spectrum would obviously be classed as invisible light. Invisible light makes up the majority of light that exists in the universe. Recall from a previous chapter that the only light your naked eye can see is the visible light which falls in-between infrared and ultraviolet radiation (see Figure 19). Infrared, ultraviolet radiation and visible (white) light all come from the sun. The different colours we see in visible light, ROY-G-BIV, are due to objects absorbing and reflecting different parts of white light. If an object is green, it is absorbing the ROY and BIV colour frequencies of visible light and reflecting G back to your eye. If an object is red, it's absorbing OY-G-BIV and reflecting R back to your eye. If an object is white it is reflecting the whole visible spectrum to your eye and doesn't absorb any colour frequencies (hence the white appearance). If an object is black, this means it's absorbing all light frequencies from the visible spectrum and reflects none. This is important to note: Black is not a colour. It is the absorption of all colours. All of the colours that make up the visible spectrum, (Red, Orange, Yellow, Green, Blue, Indigo and Violet: ROY-G-BIV) combine to form blackness. So when scientists are studying outer space to better understand the cosmos, what are they really studying?

"The color of melanin appears as Black because it is absorbing all colors. Once the color enters melanin it cannot escape. Melanin is concentrated colors, it is a cellular Black Hole similar to Black Holes in outer space." – Dr. Llaila Afrika (Melanin: What Makes Black People Black)

Science is a universal subject and therefore should be universally understood. But if it's broken down in a way that only a few can grasp, then it will lead to more confusion instead of more clarity. Why would anyone want to create more confusion in this world? According to all the evidence, people are very confused about who they are and what their purpose is in life already. This confusion is evident in the increase in people suffering from pain, anxiety, depression and other mental health issues worldwide. Adding to that confusion by not fully explaining universal concepts in a way that everyone can understand would be quite detrimental to people's lives.

"If you can't explain it simply, you don't understand it well enough." –Albert Einstein

I agree with Einstein here, but I'd take what he said one step further. I say that if someone is teaching you science and they can't explain it simply, it means they don't understand the subject well enough; or they do, they just don't want you to understand it. So they explain it to you in a complex, convoluted, confusing way. Why else would they not just explain it… simply?

"Science is simple" –Leon Marshall

To me, studying science is simply studying how the universe works. And as you are part of the universe, by studying it you'll find that you are, in essence, studying yourself. 95% of the universe is black, not dark! So isn't it time we start studying the 95%?

Melanin Quiz 8 – Melanin Confusion

1 Why is scientific terminology usually written in Latin?
  A. Because Latin America is the origin of all sciences
  B. To ensure all children who speak Latin understand it
  C. Because everyone speaks Latin
  D. To keep lay people out of the know

2 Why do most children struggle to understand science?
  A. Because they are taught science in a simplified, logical way
  B. Because they are taught science in a confusing, complex way
  C. Because they are not smart enough to understand Latin
  D. Because they don't want to learn about how the universe works

3 According to Leon Marshall, what does confusion always lead to?
  A. Harmony
  B. Conflict
  C. Peace of mind
  D. Happiness

4 What are children usually taught about melanin?
  A. It is vital to how the human body works
  B. Its main function is energy conversion
  C. It protects against the 'harmful' effects of UV radiation
  D. It can dissociate (split) water molecules into hydrogen and oxygen, like chlorophyll does in plants

5 If children are just taught one thing about melanin what might that lead to?
  A. Total confusion about what melanin actually does in their body
  B. Children not having a good understanding of melanin
  C. Children believing that the only reason why they have melanin is to protect them from the sun
  D. All the above

6 How does melanin protect DNA from the harmful effects of UV radiation?
  A. By absorbing and dissipating more than >99.9% of the UV radiation as heat. A process known as ultrafast internal conversion
  B. By blocking the sun, as sunlight is bad for your health. C'mon, you know this
  C. By releasing chalk dust into the stratosphere
  D. It doesn't! That's why we all need to wear sunscreen

7 What is the main element found in the chemical formula of melanin?
   A. Oxygen
   B. Carbon
   C. Nitrogen
   D. Hydrogen

8 What did Professor Kaba Hiawatha Kamene once call carbon?
   A. Cosmic Glue
   B. Cosmic Coal
   C. Darkness
   D. A girl's best friend

9 According to NASA, Dark Energy is?
   A. Energy emitted from the sun at night
   B. Melatonin
   C. "a complete mystery"
   D. White Light

10 What is black light?
   A. Light that is invisible to the human eye
   B. Light that is visible to the human eye
   C. "a complete mystery"
   D. "Pro-black" pseudoscience

CHAPTER NINE

MELANIN
DECODED

In my humble opinion, decoding scientific language is the key to understanding melanin. The confusion around melanin tends to come from the words, terminology or nomenclature used to describe its properties. If only we could get past the language barrier, maybe we would start to appreciate what many of the published papers have revealed about this pigment. Let's try to simplify melanin by decoding the language frequently used, with the aim of revealing what many scientists (including the ones I have featured in this book) have all proven about the "chemical key to life"

---

6 Key Points Scientifically Proven About Melanin

1. it has a broad absorption spectrum
2. it's a semiconductor
3. it's a powerful antioxidant
4. it's an energy transducer
5. it's ubiquitous
6. it can dissociate the water molecule into hydrogen and oxygen

---

1. It has a broad absorption spectrum

Melanin absorbs thousands of times more electromagnetic radiation (photons) than chlorophyll. The term radiation is synonymous with light, so when scientists say that melanin has a broad absorption spectrum it means that melanin can absorb all the different types of light frequencies that exist on the spectrum. To be more specific here, it is eumelanin that has these properties. As mentioned in the previous chapter, eumelanin shows a very broad UV-visible absorption spectrum [80], and it is able to dissipate >99.9% of the absorbed energy from sunlight radiation as heat, due to ultrafast internal conversion. Eumelanin's broad absorption spectrum means it can absorb nearly all electromagnetic frequencies it comes into contact with. It can rearrange its chemical structure to absorb the energy frequencies across the entire radiant energy spectrum, (including sunlight, X-rays, gamma rays, music, sound, radar, radio waves and microwaves) and can transmute or store this energy for later use. Melanin has the ability to neutralize the effects of potentially harmful frequencies and even convert them into something useful for the body. However, if melanin is bombarded with harmful energy frequencies on a regular basis this will undoubtedly have a negative effect on the human being. Melanin is like a battery. That battery is partially charged and can always accept an electrical charge. When sunlight or other light and sound frequencies come in contact with the melanin battery, it increases the charge of the battery to a certain degree. When the energy is captured, the battery has more energy to use inside the body. This means that essentially we can charge up our melanin by just being in the sun, listening to the right type of music, eating the right types of food or by having stimulating conversations with each other. When's the last time you felt "charged up" after a great convo with a friend?

2. It's a semiconductor

This means it conducts electricity. Simple. It aids in the flow of electrons. It is an electron transmitter. Electricity is simply the flow of an electric charge, or the flow of electrons. Anything that conducts electricity facilitates (organises and directs) the flow of electrons. The fact that most scientists call melanin a SEMI-conductor just means that it's a strong conductor of electricity under some conditions and a weak conductor under other conditions. Think of a conductor of an orchestra. What do they do? They organise and direct the flow of music. Melanin organises and directs the flow of electrical currents. In some studies, melanin has been shown to act as an insulator of electricity as well as a conductor [81]. Some scientists and researchers have even called melanin a **superconductor** (Cope. F.W.,Physiol. Chem. Phys. 10, 233 1978; Barnes, 1988, 1991; Adams, 1987) due to its ability to allow electricity to flow through it without resistance. This super conduction can occur in many parts of the body; from your eyes, to your heart, to your muscles and even your bones. Do you know that your bones are electric? The melanin in your bones makes them piezoelectric. Piezoelectricity converts mechanical energy (like running and jumping) into electrical energy. This has been coined the "piezoelectric effect" and it simply describes the fact that pressure applied to a piezoelectric material will generate a voltage. Essentially, this means applying pressure to your bones by just walking, running, jumping or dancing can generate electrical currents inside your bones that your melanin conducts. Although "piezoelectric bones" sounds like a characteristic a superhero from the marvel universe would have, it's not too far-fetched when you look at the athleticism of eumelanin-dominant individuals. Dr. Sebi is famous for saying that the body is electric. Electricity is the flow of electrons and melanin facilitates this flow in an intelligent (self-organising) way.

> *"Melanin literally conducts or carries information in an intelligent and eventually self aware organism. It underlies the earliest unfolding structures of the brain and its very nature causes it to attract light. It is the finest form of living matter we know, the crude outer sheath of bioluminescence that, when liberated in mediation and at the moment of death, opens to the clear light, which is the fundamental substructure and essence of mind and consciousness itself."* -Dr. Edward Bruce Bynum, Dark Light Consciousness - Melanin, Serpent Power, and the Luminous Matrix of Reality

3. It's a powerful antioxidant

What are antioxidants? These are compounds that help to protect the cell from damage. They do this by inhibiting oxidation. Think of oxidation as rusting or decaying. When iron or steel come into contact with water and oxygen they start to rust. When an apple is sliced in half and the inside is exposed to oxygen it starts to decay by turning brown or 'rusting'. This is due to free radicals stealing electrons from the inside of the apple. The more active the free radicals, the more the apple becomes oxidised or decays. Free radicals can occur inside of your body leading to your cells, tissues and organs becoming oxidised or decaying. Antioxidants neutralise the damaging effects of free radicals in the human body; especially the skin, keeping your skin looking firmer and younger as you age. Melanin is a powerful antioxidant; not just in humans, but in plants too. The reason why the apple turns brown initially is because the oxygen activates enzymes in the apple to produce melanin. This browning effect is not just seen in apples. It's seen in pears, bananas, avocados, eggplants and any other fruit that turns brown once the inside is exposed to oxygen. The fruit is producing melanin as an anti-oxidant. This slows down the oxidation of the fruit. So anytime you see an apple starting to brown due to being exposed to oxygen, you now know that the apple is browning as a defence mechanism to oxygen. Although oxygen is very important in cellular respiration it must be noted that oxygen is an acid. The prefix "oxy-" literally means acid and the suffix "–gen" means generating or producing. So, oxygen means "acid producing." Therefore, oxygen produces or generates acids, and too much acids can lead to cells oxidising. So 'anti-oxy-dants' prevent oxygen from causing oxidation. This is why the fruit produces melanin when exposed to oxygen and when bruised. I know, I know, hard to believe. But remember; don't believe a word I say in this book. Pick up your smartphone and make your phone smart! Research: Why do apples turn brown?

To truly grasp what antioxidants do you'll need a fuller understanding of oxygen. If you've ever studied Chemistry or Physics at a high level, you'll know that the oxygen atom is very electronegative. Electronegativity is the ability of the atom to hold onto the electrons in its orbit. Oxygen is the 8th element in the periodic table because it has 8 electrons that orbit its nucleus. It doesn't like to lose electrons from its orbit, so it holds onto them as much as possible—like a child who has been given some amazing toys to play with at kindergarten, but doesn't want to share them with the other children. That's how oxygen behaves. Even when the child with the best toys does allow other children to play with the toys, they have to play with the toys close to him and can't take them away from him. That's how oxygen behaves. And if the children do take the toys away from him you can just imagine the temper tantrum. He'll go round the kindergarten stealing them back causing conflict and damage if he has to. Yeah, that's how oxygen behaves. When oxygen loses an electron from its orbit it becomes unbalanced (see Figure 43) and goes around stealing electrons from other atoms to balance itself out. When it behaves like this in the body it's called a free radical. Free radicals can damage cells, tissues and organs by stealing energy (electrons) from them.

HEALTHY   FREE   ANTIOXIDANTS
ATOMS   RADICALS

Figure 43
Free Radicals

The technical term for this damage is oxidation. As you now know (from reading this book) oxidation is the loss of electrons. So if your cells, tissues and organs start to lose electrons, due to free radicals stealing them, they are being oxidized. This is why it's important for us to consume a diet high in antioxidants. As mentioned earlier, the foods with the highest antioxidant capacity are flavonoids that contain anthocyanins, which are usually found in dark coloured fruits like Blackcurrants, blackberries, blueberries, black beans, and black, purple and red grapes; just to name a few. Antioxidants are like the children in kindergarten who have the best toys, but at the same time are willing to share them with all the other children, so everyone can play nicely and enjoy the toys together. When the selfish child loses one of his toys and goes on a rampage to retrieve it or steal someone else's toy, the antioxidant child say's "Hey, here's my toy. You can have it." This neutralises tantrums and creates harmony inside of the kindergarten. The children can then play in a friendly environment and no children are left without toys. If that makes sense to you, and I hope it does, then you will now fully appreciate the role of antioxidants inside the human body. They stop the selfish children (free radicals) from causing damage internally by sharing their toys (electrons).

Vitamins A, C and E are very powerful antioxidants. Glutathione is one of the most powerful antioxidants our body produces and selenium is one of the most powerful antioxidants our body doesn't produce. Selenium is arguably the most important essential mineral the body needs for melanin. Consuming selenium makes melanin a more powerful antioxidant. In fact, researchers over at Northwestern University believe that they have made a breakthrough 'super antioxidant' discovery. By combining melanin with selenium they have come up with a new biomaterial that they believe could shield human tissue against X-Rays, gamma rays, UV radiation and Space Travel [82]. The team of researchers synthesised the new biomaterial, which they called "selenomelanin" and used it to treat living cells. For comparison, they also prepared cells treated with synthetic pheomelanin and eumelanin, as well as cells with no protective melanin. After receiving a dose of radiation that would be lethal to a human being, only the cells treated with selenomelanin still exhibited a normal cell cycle. What's interesting about this study is that the researchers thought they had 'discovered' something new by combining these two powerful antioxidants together. What they later found out is that selenomelanin compounds already exist in nature. "Our work points to the possibility that melanin may act as a repository for selenium, helping ensure that organisms benefit from it," said one of the leading researchers of the study. "Selenomelanin may play an important role in how selenium is metabolized and distributed biologically." They go onto say that these compounds are found in normal human proteins. If you recall, these 'selenoproteins' were mentioned in the *FOODS FOR MELANIN* chapter and they help to maintain the quality of skin and hair.

4. It's an energy transducer

When you see the word transduce associated with melanin they just mean convert. Melanin can transduce or convert one type of energy into another, similar to what plants do during photosynthesis. Plants use chlorophyll to convert one type of energy (sunlight energy) into glucose (chemical energy). According to Dr. Enqi, melanin can convert sunlight energy into electrical energy; which means it should be classified as photovoltaic. Photovoltaics is the conversion of light into electricity using semiconducting materials that exhibit the photovoltaic effect, a phenomenon studied in physics, photochemistry, and electrochemistry. Simply put, melanin can convert light (photo-) into voltage (-voltaic). This conversion of one type of energy into another is a common theme amongst melanin scholars. Dr. Richard King has mentioned many times in his books and in his lectures the fact that melanin can convert light energy to sound energy and back again. This conversion of light and sound could be one of the reasons why melanin is associated with rhythm. He mentions in his book that African people hear a wider range of sound than Europeans, in particular the low bass sounds. This might explain the ever-present low basslines in pretty much all black music, and why Africans tend to resonate more with the drum. Drums emit a low bass-sounding frequency. Melanin is capable of absorbing this frequency, through the ears and the skin, and converting it into an electrical impulse which is sent to the brain [36, 37].

Melanin's energy conversion properties are essential to human existence. It's constantly converting one form of energy into another. Similar to how your smartphone converts electrical signals into radio waves so you can talk on the phone. Speaking of smartphones, many of us rely on them for information. This information needs to be converted from one type to another depending on what you need that information for. Downloading a video from the internet is a classic example. If you've ever downloaded a video to watch it later on your computer, laptop or phone, that video needed to be converted into a format that your computer, laptop or phone could recognise. This is a form of energy conversion. The same goes for music downloads. The music you download has to be converted into a format that your phone can recognise. The format might be AAC or WMA, or the most popular music format is MP3. What if our computer devices or smartphones couldn't convert the audio file into an MP3 file? Most of us would not be able to listen to our favourite songs. That's how important energy conversion is. If you are not quite tech savvy and these file extension abbreviations are going over your head, let me try and simplify it by giving you another example. Have you ever written out a word document on your computer, clicked on the Save As button and had a look at the options? One of the options you're likely to see is Save As PDF. If you clicked this option and saved your word file as a PDF document you understand the logic of file conversion. Now take that same logic and apply it to melanin. Melanin is the ultimate energy file converter.

5. It's ubiquitous

In other words, it's found in many tissues besides the skin. When anyone (who hasn't read this book) mentions melanin, 9.999 times out of 10 they'll be talking about the melanin found in skin. Ask them why we all have melanin and inevitably they will say something along the lines of... "it protects us from the harmful effects of UV radiation." As we all know, this is true. But it should not be the only way we describe melanin. Again, that would be like telling your children that the only reason they have a digestive system is to protect them from the harmful effects of fruits and vegetables. It's disingenuous and dishonest. Children should be taught all the amazing benefits of fruits and vegetables to ensure they grow up with a healthy understanding of how these food sources aid in human health. Same with sunlight and melanin. If we just tell children that melanin protects them from the sun, then how would we explain to them melanin's presence in their bones? Do their bones need protecting from the sun? Why?

Why is a very powerful question to ask; as a wise man once said, "The important thing is to never stop questioning." That quote is by Albert Einstein, considered by many to be the greatest scientist of all time. So if Einstein says we should never stop questioning, here are some questions about melanin that need answers. Why are melanocytes located in the inner ear, nose, mouth, meninges, heart, lungs, bones, blood, armpits and organs? If we go by the very limited view of melanin being all about protection from the sun, then why would these areas, which are not directly exposed to sunlight, need melanin? Once you tap into your intuition and start using your own logic you'll find that there are many unanswered questions about melanin's main function that do not fit the widely accepted narrative. If it's all about protection from the sun, then there are some logical questions melinated men and women may want to ask themselves, like:

"Why are my nipples darker than the rest of my body?"

"If melanin's only job is to protect me from the harmful effects of the sun, why is there melanin inside my vagina?"

"Why is my penis darker than the rest of my body? It's never out in the sun!"

These questions may sound funny to you, but it's true if you think about it. Certain areas of the body never see the light of day, yet they are full of melanin. Surely there's more to this melanin thing than just protection from the sun? In some individuals, especially those who are eumelanin-dominant, their external genitals are considerably darker than the rest of their body. Science is simple! Its logic backed up by evidence. You are the evidence, so take a look and see if that's true for you.

After taking a look and realising it is true, ask yourself why then, are there huge amounts of melanin in places that don't directly interact with the sun? The answer is simple. Melanin's main function is not protection from the sun. It's the organisation of energy, hence its ubiquitous presence in the body. The conducting of electrical energy, the transduction (conversion) of different types of energy and energy transference are all examples of melanin's organising capabilities. Going back to male and female genitalia, during the sexual act there is a lot of energy transference taking place. At the exact moment a sperm penetrates an egg, the latter releases billions of zinc atoms from its surface which give off sparks. If you go online, you'll even find captured images and videos of the flash of light that sparks at the very moment a human sperm cell makes contact with an egg. This transfer of energy starts the life development cycle and it cannot occur without the presence of melanin.

Now, let's go back to the nipples. If you are eumelanin-dominant, you'll find that your nipples are dark brown and darker than the rest of your body. If you are pheomelanin-dominant, you may find that your nipples are dark pink or have a reddish hue to them. Or you may find that you, too, have dark brown nipples. We all have eumelanin and pheomelanin within us. The difference lies in the amount that the melanocyte produces of each type. Either way, your nipples, that hardly ever see the light of day (especially if you live in the northern hemisphere of the world), will be darker than the parts of your body exposed to sunlight. For women, you might've even notice that the colour of your nipples got darker during pregnancy. Why do you think that happened? Again, the answer is simple: More energy transduction. The nipples are preparing to transduce much more energy than what's usually required of them once the baby arrives. Melanin is the chemical key to life, so as life develops inside the womb melanin will undoubtedly increase to meet the demands of this new life. Melanin is heavily involved in the pregnancy process as previously discussed in the *EMBRYOGENESIS* chapter. During pregnancy many women find that they experience increased pigmentation on their face, neck, nipples and abdomen. This increase in melanin during pregnancy is known as melasma or chloasma or pregnancy mask. Now, if melanin is not the chemical key to life why would it increase during pregnancy? Why would it be so involved in the creation of life? These are just questions, and they should never stop! Thank you Mr. Einstein.

6. Melanin dissociates the water molecule into hydrogen and oxygen

This might be the most astonishing thing that melanin can do and surprisingly, it is the least talked about. Arturo Solis Herrera, a scientific director of the Centre for Human Photosynthesis Research – Mexico; has found that melanin can split the water molecule into its constituent atoms of hydrogen and oxygen. In science, this is known as dissociation: breaking apart the bonds of molecules. Historically, the general consensus in the scientific community, when it came to dissociating the water molecule, was that only plants could do this complex task during the process of photosynthesis. But according to Dr. Herrera and his team of researchers, they have found that melanin can split water molecules quite easily and this is actually the real way energy is produced and maintained in the human body. If that wasn't remarkable enough, through their extensive research they also found that melanin can re-form the water molecule after splitting it. Herrera and his team have published many research papers about melanin over the years, to prove to the world melanin's true function. In one of the papers, entitled: *Energy Production, the Main Role of Melanin in the Mesencephalon* [83] they say the following:

> Our finding of the intrinsic property of melanin to split and re-form the water molecule constitutes a disruptive knowledge. Our body is able to take energy from light, therefore has the astonishing capacity to use water as a source of electrons, a previously unknown fact.

138

	Chlorophyll	Melanin
Water dissociation	Yes	Yes
Take up energy from light	Yes	Yes
Visible light	Yes	Yes
Invisible light	No	Yes
Take place during the day	Yes	Yes
Take place during night	No	Yes
Re-form the water molecule	No	Yes
Occurs inside cell	Yes	Yes
Occurs outside cell	No	Yes
Produces H_2	Yes	Yes
Produces O_2	Yes	Yes
Produces high energy electrons	No	Yes
Could be the origin of life	No	Yes

This table is taken straight from the published paper and it shows how they compared melanin to chlorophyll. The similarities are strikingly obvious. These profound similarities made Dr. Herrera state confidently in his book, *The Human Photosynthesis,* that the very first step of life in plants and humans is the same: the dissociation of the water molecule. Although these pigments are very similar, Herrera highlights the fact that chlorophyll can only split the water molecule irreversibly; which means that although both melanin and chlorophyll can split water into hydrogen and oxygen, it is only melanin that can reform it.

If you have never studied science before, you might be asking yourself, "So what? What's the fascination with splitting water?" Those who have a science background might think that splitting water into hydrogen and oxygen will allow your body to use the oxygen gas to help with cellular respiration (aerobic metabolism). According to Dr. Herrera and his team however, oxygen is not the star of the show in water. It's actually hydrogen that the body needs for energy. Hydrogen is the universal energy carrier. Energy carriers allow the transport of energy in a usable form from one place to another. Hydrogen is the primary sustainable source of renewable energy in the world. As a fuel, it can be used for electricity production, solar powered applications and wind powered applications. Hydrogen can even be used as a fuel in internal combustion engines to replace diesel or petrol. Every living organism on Earth relies on the renewable energy carrier known to man as hydrogen. And every living organism on Earth gets its supply of hydrogen from the same place: WATER. When melanin splits the water molecule the body can then use the hydrogen to power cellular metabolism, like the production of ATP (adenosine triphosphate). It is well known in science that ATP is the cell's energy currency. What they fail to tell us is that ATP relies on a gradient of hydrogen ions to operate and create new ATP molecules. And this gradient of hydrogen ions comes from the splitting and reforming of the water molecule by melanin. This splitting and reforming action can be compared to an on/off switch in an electric circuit. In a separate research paper published in 2017, Dr. Herrera compares this action to the universal computer binary code of 1's and 0's.

The way in which melanin dissociates and re-associates the water molecule that is: liguid-gas could be represented as 0 and 1, like a binary code, which abound in nature. Therefore, it is possible that the melanin not only delivers energy, but also information.

Now here's where I'd like you, the reader, to put your thinking cap on. I personally think that science is simple. To me, its logic backed up by evidence. Logic is something that we are all born with, like a gift from the universe. For example, you don't have to be told over and over again that 2+2 = 4. Your logic tells you that it's true. So let's start putting two and two together here. Dr Auturo Solis Herrera has proven scientifically that melanin splits the water molecule into hydrogen and oxygen. He believes this splitting and reforming of the water molecule drives cellular energy. Compare this to what Dr. Gerald Pollack has revealed through his work about water. Dr. Pollack has proven that sunlight and heat 'structure' water by separating the negatively charged ions in water from the positively charged ions, creating a liquid battery. He believes that this charge separation is what drives cellular energy. What does that sound like? Is anyone putting two and two together here? Is it me or does it sound like these two knowledgeable scientists are explaining the same phenomenon, just using different language? I'm not as smart as these two scholars, nor have I ever studied the effects of melanin in a laboratory setting; however, it sounds to me like melanin might be able to structure water and this is what powers our cells. The hydrophilic nature of eumelanin combined with its ability to absorb, store and transduce electromagnetic radiation makes me come to the logical conclusion that it is highly efficient at structuring water.

When we are exposed to infrared light, eumelanin splits and reforms water molecules inside of us like an electric on/off switch that the body utilises as and when necessary; and this is what powers every biochemical process in the body. If this is true, why on Earth do we not teach this in all schools to every child? This is just as important as teaching children about chlorophyll and photosynthesis. Can you imagine if we taught children how plants live and grow without mentioning chlorophyll's involvement in photosynthesis? Children would be so confused about plants. Now apply that same logic to teaching children about how humans live and grow without mentioning melanin's involvement in cellular energy. Total confusion!

Melanin Quiz 9 – Melanin Decoded

1 Melanin is known to have a broad absorption spectrum. What does this mean?
- **A.** It can absorb many different types of electromagnetic frequencies, from visible to invisible
- **B.** It can only absorb visible frequencies from the electromagnetic spectrum
- **C.** It can only absorb invisible frequencies from the electromagnetic spectrum
- **D.** It doesn't absorb any frequencies, it blocks them instead

2 Studies have shown that melanin is a semiconductor of electricity. What does this mean?
- **A.** It can only act as an insulator of electricity
- **B.** It cannot conduct electricity
- **C.** It can act as a conductor and insulator of electricity
- **D.** It blocks the flow of electrons

3 Melanin is a powerful antioxidant. What do antioxidants do?
- **A.** They neutralise the damaging effects of free radicals
- **B.** They inhibit oxidation
- **C.** They donate electrons to free radicals
- **D.** All the above

4 Why does an apple turn brown when it's cut in half?
- **A.** Because the apple is producing melanin as an antioxidant
- **B.** To slow down the oxidation of the apple
- **C.** As a defence mechanism to oxygen
- **D.** All the above

5 Melanin is an energy transducer? What does this mean?
- **A.** It can convert a word document into a PDF
- **B.** It can translate scientific jargon into common sense
- **C.** It can convert one form of energy into another
- **D.** It can translate English into French

6 Melanin has been described as being ubiquitous. What does this mean?
- **A.** It's found throughout the whole body
- **B.** It's only found in the skin
- **C.** It's only found in the eyes
- **D.** It's only found in black people

7 According to Arturo Solis Herrera, the melanin in our body can?
- **A.** Split the water molecule into hydrogen and oxygen
- **B.** Re-form the water molecule
- **C.** Use water as a source of electrons
- **D.** All the above

CHAPTER TEN

CODE OF SILENCE

One thing I have noticed over the many years of researching this subject, is that there seems to be a **melanin code of silence** amongst academics in the science community. An unwritten rule that academics, doctors and those in the medical industry seem to abide by. The rule is to never mention the true functions of melanin to the general public. Keep information about melanin hidden and only talk about it in terms of skin protection. Where's the evidence of this? Well, it is not taught in great detail in schools, colleges or universities despite its biological importance to all living organisms. When it is mentioned, the person talking about melanin always seems to focus on the protective properties of melanin in relation to UV radiation and DNA, conveniently neglecting all other properties. Maybe they just don't know about the other properties, one might surmise. Well in that case, I truly thank the great teachers who came before me, plus this magical universe for inspiring me to write this book. Hopefully after reading this book 'experts' won't continue to just mention the protective aspects of melanin and possibly start talking about how melanin is involved in embryogenesis and how neuromelanin facilitates all of our senses and nerve impulses. Or how melanin splits water molecules into hydrogen and oxygen, just like chlorophyll does in plants. Or how melanin is a semi-conductor of electricity within the human body. Perhaps, after reading this book the science community will change the narrative around UV radiation and begin to teach students about melanin's broad absorption spectrum. As you know now, it is extremely efficient at absorbing electromagnetic radiation, especially UV rays. UV radiation is present in sunlight and constitutes about 10% of the total electromagnetic radiation output from the sun. This is one of the main aspects of melanin that I think children are taught in a very confusing way. They are told about all the dangers of ultraviolet radiation. And rightly so, as the high frequencies of the different types of UV rays could potentially damage DNA and lead to skin cancer, especially in pheomelanin-dominant individuals [84]. Children should be taught this, of course. But shouldn't they be taught about the benefits of these high frequencies as well? What benefits? Well, let's first do a quick breakdown of the different types of UV radiation.

Benefits of UV Radiation

There are three types of ultraviolet radiation known to man. UVA, UVB and UVC. These are all invisible to the human eye. UVA is the most common type as it's responsible for up to 95% of all UV light that penetrates the Earth's atmosphere and reaches our skin. It is present all year round. As long as there's daylight, there's UVA. These are the longest waves on the UV spectrum and they're capable of penetrating deep into the skin. Roughly 80% of UVA rays reach the outer layer of the dermis, the layer of skin beneath the epidermis, making UVA the most penetrable of all three types. UVA can even penetrate through glass and 9 feet of water. UVB on the other hand, are the medium waves that are strongest during the summer months and are most commonly associated with tanning. These medium-penetrating, shorter wavelengths are absorbed by transparent glass, but most of the UVB contained in daylight is absorbed by the ozone layer, resulting in less than 5% reaching the Earth's surface. Lastly, UVC are the shortest wavelengths in the UV spectrum. The short-waves of UVC have the weakest penetrating ability and according to most research the UVC contained in sunlight is almost completely absorbed by the ozone layer before it reaches the Earth's surface. If you were to do some research online about the health benefits of UV radiation you'll find that the benefits are quite impressive. Studies show that UVA decreases blood pressure considerably by activating Nitric Oxide (NO) in the skin. NO vasodilates (widens) the blood vessels, leading to increased blood circulation and improved cardiovascular health. NO is so effective at widening the blood vessels that the medical industry frequently use it in drugs to help people with heart problems. It's also used in erectile dysfunction drugs to aid in increased blood flow to the penis. This is why Viagra is so potent, because it activates Nitric Oxide. Imagine if men knew they could achieve this potency with sunlight. The benefits of sunlight-induced NO seem to be endless. A study published in the Journal of Virology back in 2005 found that NO inhibits the replication cycle of severe acute respiratory syndrome coronavirus (SARS-CoV) [85]. In layman's terms, this just means it reduces respiratory tract infections by inactivating the virus. Many people do not know the benefits of Nitric Oxide because we are not taught about any health aspects of UVA radiation. Nor are we taught about the importance of UVB radiation which is needed for vitamin D synthesis, despite the vital significance of vitamin D to our health. Let's remind ourselves of how vitamin D is produced.

How is Vitamin D produced?

1. Exposed skin absorbs UVB rays
2. Cholesterol in skin gets converted into a pre-vitamin D
3. Pre-Vitamin D gets processed through the Liver and Kidneys
4. Kidneys synthesise it into the active form of vitamin D that the body uses

Vitamin D Code of Silence

Vitamin D is so vitally important to human health that nearly every cell in your body has VDR's or Vitamin D Receptors [86]. As the name suggests, VDR's are little receptors on the outside of the cell membrane that give the cell the ability to receive vitamin D. What is Vitamin D and why does nearly every cell in your body need to receive it? Vitamin D is absolutely essential for a tremendous number of biological functions, including the most well-known function of facilitating the absorption of calcium in the gut to build strong bones. An insufficient supply of vitamin D could lead to a whole host of bone issues including rickets and osteoporosis. This is well documented and universally taught by the science community. However, vitamin D is another area of science where some scientists have decided to follow a code of silence around its true power. There is so much confusion around vitamin D which never gets addressed. For example, let's start with its name. Vitamin D. Look up the word vitamin online and you'll find that a vitamin is an organic molecule that is an essential micronutrient, which an organism needs in small quantities for proper functioning of its metabolism. This definition does not fit the macronutrient needed by nearly every single cell in your body (Vitamin D). Furthermore, essential micronutrients are required in small amounts in the diet because they cannot be synthesised in the body. This once again, does not describe the properties of vitamin D which can **only** be synthesised in the body. Once you understand what vitamin D actually does in the body and realise that its functions do not follow the typical definitions of a 'vitamin' you may start questioning its name. And you wouldn't be the first one to question it. Back in the 1980's, a University professor by the name of Walter Stumpf came to the conclusion that vitamin D was not a vitamin at all! He noticed that vitamin D experts during this time were only writing and researching the calcitropic (calcium) effect of vitamin D in the body. So, he decided to study the non-calcitropic (heart, lung, brain, pancreas, stomach, muscle, immune, etc.) effects of vitamin D whilst working at the University of North Carolina School of Medicine. His findings left him with no choice but to call vitamin D a 'panacea' of the sun and he renamed it Soltriol, the 'hormone of sunshine.' Excited about what he had discovered, he worked vigorously to publish his results for the world to see. However, the academic vitamin D powers that existed during that time would not let this scientist publish his results in mainstream journals, nor let him give talks at mainstream meetings. For decades his findings were never released to the public until in 2012 he decided to detail his experiences in an editorial paper he entitled: *Vitamin D and the scientific calcium dogma: understanding the 'Panacea' of the sun* [87]

In the paper, he reports that vitamin D (Soltriol) is a:

• Hormone of reproduction and fertility
• Hormone of growth and development
• Hormone of immune and stress response
• Hormone of the digestive system
• Hormone of endocrine regulation
• Hormone of central nervous system

This steroid hormone solely relies on UV irradiation for synthesis. Skin exposure to UVB light is the only way your liver and kidneys can synthesise the active form of Vitamin D3 (SOLTRIOL). According to Walter Stumpf, vitamin D is exceptional because of its extensive multiple actions, its high tolerance and its prophylactic and therapeutic potentials. Vitamin D's wide-ranging life-sustaining effects set it apart from other steroids, as well as all other compounds and drugs. He concludes that vitamin D (Soltriol) is as fundamental as the sun, the closest we have to a 'panacea.' In the *FOODS FOR MELANIN* chapter I recommended feeding your melanin with more sunlight in order to top up your vitamin D levels, which seems obvious as UVB rays from the sun activate the vitamin D process. It's actually a win-win situation when you feed your melanin with more sunlight, because the UVB rays will indirectly lower cholesterol by converting the cholesterol found in the skin (7-dehydrocholesterol) into the vitamin D precursor. UVB exposure from the sun seems to be the most natural way to increase the "active form" of vitamin D inside the body. This "active form" (SOLTRIOL) is what the cells use for various biological reasons.

PRODUCTION OF VITAMIN D

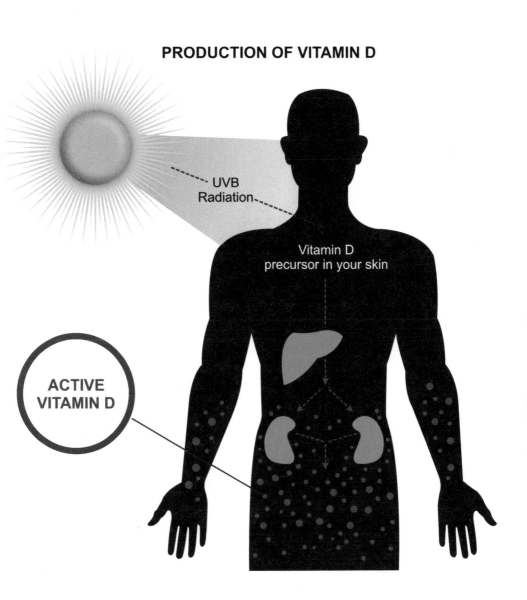

Figure 44
How Vitamin D is Produced

Vitamin D Supplementation Code of Silence

Despite the logic and evidence of how soltriol is produced, many black people would rather take a vitamin D supplement than bask in the sun. Their reasoning behind this is that there's not a lot of sunshine where they live so they have to rely on supplementation. This would make total sense if supplementation worked. However, various studies are now confirming that vitamin D supplements are not living up to the hype and that the way we test for vitamin D deficiency needs to be revised [88-90]. Some studies have reported that although Black adults typically have low levels of vitamin D in their blood, they are on par with whites when it comes to the "active form" of vitamin D used by the body's cells. Experts believe these findings go a long way toward explaining a paradox: Blacks usually have fairly low vitamin D levels, but have greater bone mass than whites. How is that possible when vitamin D is needed to maintain strong bones? The science community could never rationalise this paradox before, until now. Studies are now revealing that testing vitamin D levels in the blood alone is not an accurate indication of the active form of vitamin D used by the cells [88-90]. In one of the studies, Dr. Ravi Thadhani, a professor of medicine at Massachusetts General Hospital, suggested that doctors may be overdiagnosing vitamin D deficiency in black patients. "We're suggesting that the definition of vitamin D deficiency needs to be rethought," said Thadhani, whose report appeared in the Nov. 21 issue of the New England Journal of Medicine. Right now, doctors use a blood test that measures a person's total 25-hydroxyvitamin D level (the non-active form of vitamin D). And if you consider just that total level, up to 80 percent of Black Americans would be labelled vitamin D deficient. If they are vitamin D deficient, surely they should have the worst bone health?

The Truth About Vitamin D

"The population in the United States with the best bone health happens to be the African-American population," said Dr. Thadhani. "But almost 80 percent of these individuals are defined as having vitamin D deficiency. This was perplexing." These results suggest that black people in the US may not be deficient in the "active form" of vitamin D after all. What about black people in other parts of the world, like the UK for example? Many black people in the UK believe that supplementation is the solution to a lack of sunshine, and wholeheartedly believe the doctors diagnosis of their vitamin D deficiency when in fact, according to these new studies, their "active form" of SOLTRIOL is probably just as high as whites; if not higher. Sometimes we don't need a science 'expert' to tell us what we already know. Sometimes just using common sense and following logic is all we need. If what we are taught about vitamin D is true, then one of its main functions is to regulate the uptake of calcium for strong bones. You don't need a science degree to see who has strong bones. Just look at sport. There's no way a human being (or even an animal) can run fast or jump high without extremely strong bone density. The mechanical force exerted on the skeletal system through the vigorous acts of running, jumping and changing direction quickly would be too much for anyone with weak bone density to handle. Sport then, becomes the indisputable evidence that reveals the lies we are told about "Blacks" naturally having lower vitamin D levels. And not just sport. According to Professor Stumpf the sunshine hormone they call vitamin D is a hormone that aids in reproduction and fertility. Again, you don't need a science degree to work out who the most fertile women in the world are. Just look at who's having the most babies and research which group of women lead in infertility treatments. Soltriol is also a hormone that aids in growth and development. Various studies suggest that black infants grow and develop at a faster rate than white infants [91, 92]. These are things that are never discussed openly and honestly by the science community today. What is behind the fear of allowing people to know the truth about vitamin D? What would the truth lead to?

UV Light and Melanin Code of Silence

UVB light is absolutely essential to vitamin D synthesis. Without it, we would not be able to process the "active form" which our cells use. This should be common knowledge. UVA light naturally lowers blood pressure by stimulating the release of Nitric Oxide from skin stores. This too, should be common knowledge. However, modern society tends to follow the same unwritten code of silence that the science community follow when it comes to the benefits of ultraviolet radiation. The benefits are minimised (or not talked about at all) whilst the dangers are amplified. When are we going to start having open and honest conversations about UV light and melanin? Explaining the difference between eumelanin and pheomelanin would be a good start. Eumelanin has a natural ability to absorb UV rays and protect DNA from damage at the same time. As you now know from reading this book, it does this by transforming the energy into harmless amounts of heat through a process called "ultrafast internal conversion." Pheomelanin is a much less efficient absorber of UV light. Additionally, UV irradiation of pheomelanin produces free radicals, which can cause damage to DNA cells leading to melanoma. A 2009 published report entitled *The Protective Role of Melanin Against UV Damage in Human Skin*, found that pheomelanin is especially prone to photodegradation [93-95] and is thought to contribute to the damaging effects of UV radiation because it can generate hydrogen peroxide and superoxide anions [96-98] and might cause mutations in melanocytes or other cells [99]. The report also found that pheomelanin increases the release of histamine, which contributes to the sun-induced erythema and edema in fair-skinned individuals [100]. The authors are quoted as saying, "Thus, it is possible that pheomelanin has a weak carcinogenic effect that can contribute to melanoma formation…" The science community are well aware of these studies and this could be why they incessantly warn us about the dangers of UV light over and over again. This is quite noble of them, considering the dangers UV radiation poses to pheomelanin-dominant individuals. However, wouldn't it be a good idea to educate people on the different types of melanin so individuals have a better understanding of how their skin interacts with light? The different types of light frequencies, from ultraviolet to infrared, all have an impact on our health and biological systems. The fact that we all have different skin tones proves that we all interact with light frequencies differently. Thus, knowing the benefits and the risks of these light frequencies would allow the individual to make better choices about their skin health. I truly hope that the code of silence around UV radiation is lifted one day, so that we can all fully appreciate the benefits (and risks) of this type of light energy.

The Elephant in the Room

The melanin code of silence that I've observed from the scientific community is very apparent when you listen to any scientific discussion about human health, cellular energy, biochemistry and / or neuroscience. Melanin seems to be the elephant in the room that never gets mentioned, even though the elephant is so large it takes up pretty much all the space in the room. Take sport for example. Notice how melanin is never mentioned in any sporting context, despite the obvious complexion of the best athletes in the world and the fact that success in any sport is primarily based on efficient motor abilities (movement). The substantia nigra is one of the 12 melanin centers in the brain that is responsible for efficient motor functions. This 'black substance' is full of dopamine neurons which controls movement and motivation, two things that would help any athlete succeed in sport. But you'll never hear that mentioned by a sports commentator at the Olympics. Soltriol increases the absorption of calcium which leads to strong powerful bones that are able to withstand the enormous mechanical force exerted on them through the motor activities of running and jumping. Melanin absorbs UVB light leading to tremendous amounts of soltriol in the body, which would explain the elite athletes super human abilities to run fast and jump high in sports such as Sprinting and Basketball. But this is never mentioned. Ask any sporting expert why eumelanin-dominant athletes can run so fast and jump high and watch how they tiptoe around the elephant. Fertility, as mentioned earlier, is another example. Notice how melanin is never mentioned in any fertility conversations despite numerous studies proving, without a shadow of a doubt, that the most fertile women on Earth are found in various parts of Africa [101]. You now know from reading this book that melanin is heavily involved in the embryogenesis process; from start (a melanin sheath covers both the sperm and the egg) to finish (during gastrulation all organs develop from three layers of skin: ectoderm, mesoderm and endoderm). To have a scientific discussion about fertility without mentioning melanin would be like scientifically discussing vitamin D without mentioning the sun. It would be very dishonest. Melanin is key to the life creation process. It is essential to every living organism on this planet, and maybe off this planet too.

Space Travel Code of Silence

Did you know that the use of melanin is essential to space travel? So much so, that it would be impossible to even launch a space craft into space without the abundant use of melanin to coat all essential electronics inside the shuttle for protection against high energy radiation. According to Professor Carol Barnes (1988), the US Space shuttle makes liberal use of melanin in all of its cable assemblies. As mentioned earlier in this book, selenomelanin seems to be the melanin of choice for these coatings as it has shown extreme radiation shielding properties that could offer protection against X-Rays, Gamma Rays and UV radiation during space travel. A 2019 report stated that NASA was looking into sending melanin samples into space for six months to test how well melanin holds up in space. According to the report, their concern was with ionizing radiation, referring to electromagnetic rays from the sun, like ultraviolet, gamma rays and X-rays. They felt that the astronauts would need extreme protecting from ionizing radiation and particulate radiation — the fast moving sub-atomic particles of electrons and protons. Both forms of radiation can damage electronic devices and interact with materials, like a spacesuit, to generate secondary radiation. According to these researchers, selenomelanin provides the best form of protection against the high frequency ionizing rays that astronauts may encounter whilst in outer space. I guess these researchers were not told about the incredible spaceflight of Apollo 11. Surely NASA already knows what they are going to encounter whilst in outer space because, you know, they've been out there before. Was melanin used to coat Apollo 11? Is the ionizing radiation that Neil Armstrong and friends encountered in 1969 much greater now? These are just questions that will never be answered due to the melanin code of silence. Astronauts, doctors, scientists and even billionaires all seem to be following the code. Billionaires are now working closely with scientists to see if space travel can become an industry within itself. Have you noticed this trend? Billionaires like Richard Branson, Jeff Bezos and Elon Musk, all of which have privately financed space exploration programs, are well invested in the emerging market of space tourism. What is behind their fascination and dedication to explore space? Billionaires seem to be competing to see who can conquer the galaxy first. How on Earth will this help humanity? With all the things a billionaire could spend their money on to make this world a better place, it seems slightly odd that their focus would be on venturing out of this world. Regardless of their reasons to visit Mars and beyond, the use of melanin to coat their space shuttle electronics will become more and more of a necessity. Who knows, soon traveling to the moon in a melanin-coated spacecraft might be a regular holiday trip for the rich. This may sound far-fetched to you, but rest assured billionaires and scientists are working night and day to make frequent space travel a reality. This concept cannot come to fruition without the elephant in the room (or should I say, the elephant in the shuttle).

Henrietta Lacks Code of Silence

Melanin samples and human cells have historically been used to test the effects of space radiation. The first human cells sent to space were HeLa cells. What are HeLa cells? HeLa, pronounced hee-lah, are cells that were taken from the body of a black woman named Henrietta Lacks back in 1951. At the time, Henrietta Lacks, a 31-year-old mother of five, was a patient at Johns Hopkins hospital in Baltimore getting treatment for cervical cancer. Whilst she was undergoing surgery, which she ultimately died from, her doctor removed cells from her tumour for medical research. Two days after her death, a lab attendant discovered that the cells they had taken from her tumour were growing. This marked the first instance of continuous growth of human cells outside the body. These 'ever-growing' cells would go on to transform modern medicine and were given the name 'immortal' as the cells never died. Lacks's cells – known as HeLa, using the first two letters of each of her names – became the first immortal human cell line in history. To date, her cells, which have been used in more than 80,000 studies, are the only immortal cell line being used for scientific breakthroughs. Advanced research for gene mapping, cloning, in-vitro fertilization (IVF), influenza, Parkinson's disease and leukaemia cures were major contributions developed from her cells. All these health milestones, and many more, owe everything to the life, and death, of a young black mother.

For the world of medical research, the use of Henrietta Lacks' cells has been a scientific miracle. Where would medical advances be without the use of HeLa cells? Cultivation of HeLa launched a revolution in biomedical research and a multi-billion dollar industry. The cells were sold all over the world, and led to important discoveries in fighting some of the deadliest diseases known to mankind. It must be noted that Lacks never agreed to her cells being used for research. For years, her own family had no idea that her cells were still alive in petri dishes in scientists' labs all over the world. Her own children only found out due to her genome being sequenced and made public in 2013. Before then, her children had no idea that their mother's cells were being used for medical breakthroughs, creating a multibillion dollar industry which the science community has benefitted from for the past six decades. Lacks' children have not shared in any of the huge profits derived from their mother's cells, nor have they been offered any financial compensation. To this day they still struggle to come to terms with the fact that their mother's cells are still alive. They have been deeply traumatized by the whole ordeal and it's taken a toll on some of the family members' health. To make matters worse, none of Lacks' children had health insurance. Deborah Lacks, the daughter of Henrietta, often expressed her anxiety and pain of never really knowing her mother. This undoubtedly had an impact on her health and after years of her health deteriorating, she died from a stroke in 2009.

The full Henrietta Lacks story seems to be shrouded in mystery. The secrecy surrounding the stolen cells of a poor, young black woman has led many to believe that there is indeed a code of silence in the science community, especially around black women's cells. Why didn't they tell the Lacks family what they were doing with HeLa cells? Why keep it a secret for decades, whilst making millions, perhaps billions of dollars profit from the selling of her cells worldwide? Is there anything else we, the public, should know about these immortal cells that are still alive today? Are we to believe that Henrietta Lacks is the only black woman with immortal cells or could it be possible that there are others with similar genetics? If there were other black women with immortal cells would the science community make this public or would they hide this information like they did with HeLa cells? These are questions we should continue to ask to break the code of silence that exists in this industry.

According to Rebecca Skloot, author of *The Immortal Life of Henrietta Lacks*, so much of science started with her cells. HeLa cells were used to test the effects of atomic radiation, and they were sent into outer space for experimentation on zero gravity in 1960. Ever since then, HeLa cell lines have been used in more than 100,000 scientific PubMed publications on a range of topics including cancer, cell biology, genetics, and infectious diseases. These immortal cells are still the highest-ranking research cell used throughout all major medical research complexes around the world. They were even used to study the effects of SARS-CoV-2 on humans, providing inputs for the development of a COVID-19 vaccine [102-104]. So much of what we know today in science is due to HeLa cells. They have been instrumental to what we know about viruses, bacteria and toxins in our environment. However, the burning question of "What makes them immortal?" has never been answered. Meanwhile, year after year the elephant sits in the corner of the science lab wondering if anyone is going to mention it.

Bioelectronics Code of Silence

Ever since scientists discovered eumelanin's ability to conduct electricity they have been looking for ways to take advantage of this trait. This has led to the study of bioelectronics becoming very popular over recent years. Bioelectronics, sometimes called the next medical frontier, is a research field that combines electronics and biology to develop miniaturized implantable devices capable of altering and controlling electrical signals in the human body. Recent studies have found that eumelanin conducts enough electricity to enable electronic devices that could be implanted in humans, so it has become the focus of bioelectronic research. A multi-discipline team of scientists from Italy have figured out how to boost eumelanin's conductivity to the point that it may become usable as a coating for medical implants and other devices that human bodies won't reject [105]. Other scientists from around the world are doing similar research. Scientists from Carnegie Mellon University (CMU) in Pittsburgh USA, have developed a digestible battery made from melanin, which they say can power a tiny 5 milliwatt device for 18 hours. The device would be swallowed to diagnose and treat diseases of all kind. They believe that these "smart pills" would make medications much more efficient and safer to use for people with underlying health conditions. The traditional method of using tubes and needles to diagnose and treat ill patients could become a thing of the past if these medical batteries, made from melanin, become the new norm. In order for this to transform a new reality, the way medical students are taught how to diagnose and treat diseases will have to be updated. Students will need to learn how these new bioelectronics interact with human cells. A new branch of scientific study will undoubtedly emerge from this. Robo-Biology? Digi-Chemistry? Electro-Ceuticals? I'm not sure what they will call this new type of 'smart' science. But make no mistake; a new field of science is on the horizon. Who knows, soon we might see University's all over the world start offering courses like an MSc in Digital Chemistry. Digitologists may be required for all hospitals in the near future. This may birth a new industry altogether, the "Digital Health Care" industry perhaps. Will this be a great step for humanity? A world where human beings ingest melanin batteries to help them cope with diseases. It sounds like a good thing, right? Especially considering the millions of people with health issues around the world that could potentially benefit from this new medical treatment. The demand for these types of batteries would go through the roof! One can only surmise the amount of melanin batteries that the 'Digital Health Care' industry would need to manufacture in order to keep up with the demand. It really looks like this is the direction that science is heading. You've heard of smart phones, well get ready for Smart Humans: powered by electronic batteries (or chips?), designed to diagnose and treat disease in a 'smart', more efficient and effortless way. Now, I wouldn't consider myself as smart as the scientists that will design these batteries, but I am logical. And as a logical human being I have a logical question. Where are they going to get all that melanin from to make the batteries?

silence

Melanin Quiz 10 – The Melanin Code of Silence

1 **What type of UV radiation naturally lowers blood pressure by stimulating the release of Nitric Oxide from skin stores?**
   A. UVA
   B. UVB
   C. UVC
   D. UVD

2 **What type of UV radiation is needed for Vitamin D synthesis?**
   A. UVA
   B. UVB
   C. UVC
   D. UVD

3 **Where can VDR's (Vitamin D Receptors) be found?**
   A. Only in the bones
   B. Only in the skin
   C. All throughout the body
   D. Only in the kidneys

4 **According to Professor Walter Stumpf, Vitamin D (Soltriol) is not a vitamin, but it's actually a...?**
   A. Hormone of reproduction and fertility
   B. Hormone of growth and development
   C. Hormone of immune and stress response
   D. All the above

5 **Why is cholesterol important for Vitamin D synthesis?**
   A. It is the precursor to Vitamin D
   B. It blocks Vitamin D synthesis
   C. It protects the skin from the 'harmful' effects of UV radiation
   D. It's not important

6 **What is the issue with testing black peoples Vitamin D levels?**
   A. The test doesn't measure the non-active form of Vitamin D
   B. The test doesn't measure the "active form" of Vitamin D
   C. The test doesn't measure Vitamin D levels at all
   D. There is no issue with Vitamin D testing

7 **What type of melanin is prone to DNA damage from UV radiation?**
    A.   Pheomelanin
    B.   Eumelanin
    C.   Neuromelanin
    D.   Selenomelanin

8 **According to NASA, what type of melanin provides the best form of protection against the high frequency ionizing rays that astronauts may encounter whilst in outer space?**
    A.   Pheomelanin
    B.   Eumelanin
    C.   Neuromelanin
    D.   Selenomelanin

9 **The immortal cells of a black woman named Henrietta Lacks have been used for what scientific breakthroughs?**
    A.   Space Radiation, Gene mapping, Cloning, IVF, Influenza,
    B.   Parkinson's Disease, Leukaemia Cures, Cancer Treatments
    C.   Development of the Covid-19 Vaccines
    D.   All the above

CHAPTER ELEVEN

MELANIN AND MARIJAUNA

MELANIN AND MARIJAUNA

One of the biggest codes of silence around the effects of melanin is the effect it has on drugs, toxic chemicals and heavy metals. Due to its stable nature, melanin has the unique ability to bind to harmful drugs, toxins and metals and retain these harmful compounds in its structure for a very long time (Larsson and Tjalve, 1979). Various scientists (Lindquist, Larsson and Lyden-Sokolowski, 1987) have suggested that melanin's capacity to accumulate and bind to a variety of compounds could protect the cells that harbour the pigment by keeping potentially harmful substances confined. They also suggest that melanin would, over time, release these substances slowly in low, non-toxic concentrations. According to Dr. T. Owens Moore, author of *Pigment Power* and other melanin-based books, this slow release may cause certain drugs (e.g. cocaine) to have greater potency in highly melinated individuals. After reading this, one might come to the conclusion that the influence of drugs, heavy metals and other toxic chemicals in the body could potentially cause different physiological effects in eumelanin-dominant individuals and pheomelanin-dominant individuals. The massive implications this has on the medical industry should be carefully considered.

Each individual's melanin type and amount ought to be taken into consideration when recommendations by a medical professional are made about the individuals' dietary needs, pharmaceutical needs or medical needs. It has been shown that melanin will bind to any chemical that has a similar chemical structure to it. Professor Carol Barnes, a top research chemist, confirmed this finding in his book MELANIN: *The Chemical Key To Black Greatness*. In this book he mentions that toxic drugs such as cocaine, LSD, and marijuana are very similar to melanin and the sub-units that make up melanin (tyrosine, melatonin, other alkaloids). These similarities in chemical structure cause the addicting and toxifying effects of these drugs. He states that melanin can become toxic to the human because it combines with harmful drugs such as cocaine, amphetamines, psycholic hallucinogens, neuroleptics (tranquilizers), marijuana, "agent orange" (dioxane), paraquats, tetracyclines, etc. Melanin is so effective at binding to chemicals with similar molecular structures to its own that it may hold onto these chemicals longer than necessary, causing a detrimental effect on the individual's long-term health.

Drug Testing

When I first discovered this property of melanin it made me wonder if this is the reason why eumelanin-dominant individuals can test positive for a drug like marijuana, weeks or even months after they have stopped using it. It made me think back to all the times I've heard mainstream media go out of their way to mention that a black person, usually an athlete or a suspected criminal, tested positive for THC.

THC (tetrahydrocannabinol) is the active ingredient in marijuana, which is responsible for marijuana's psychoactive side effects such as euphoria, dizziness and intensified visual and auditory sensations. Simply put, it's what gives you the feeling of being high. After putting on my investigative hat and doing some research it turns out my speculations were right. There's been numerous studies to suggest that Black people can test positive for a drug, months or even years after stopping the use of it. Back in the 80's, forensic scientists from Atlanta even discovered that Black people could test positive for marijuana without ever taking it. In an article published in the May (1986) edition of Jet Magazine, forensic chemist James Woodford revealed cases where eumelanin-dominant individuals failed marijuana tests despite later being proven to be drug free. Here's an excerpt from the article:

> Blacks and other naturally dark-skinned people may be getting shafted when they flunk urine tests that indicate marijuana abuse because they possess high levels of the pigment melanin, which is chemically similar to the ingredient in marijuana. Furthermore, melanin actually soaks up chemical compounds similar to tetrahydrocannabinol (THC), the active ingredient in marijuana.
> James Woodford, a forensic chemist from Atlanta, and associate Steve Swimmer, also of Atlanta, have studied cases where Blacks were suspected of using marijuana and fired from their jobs after they maintained their innocence. Hosea Williams, Atlanta City Councilman and civil rights activist, supports their stand. Woodford and Swimmer are working with dozens of people who have been suspected of abusing marijuana and later lost their jobs. "Virtually all of them are Black," Swimmer declared.

Woodford would go onto explain in the article that the urine tests for marijuana had a 10 to 15 percent margin of error and were not as accurate as many manufacturers contend their tests to be. Noting that no two laboratories are operated the same way. Woodford contends everyone possesses some degree of melanin in the blood, brain and urine. In fact, medicines such as Advil (ibuprofen), Nuprin and some natural dietary substances have chemicals that resemble THC and can show up falsely on tests. Woodford called many marijuana tests "non-specific tests."

> "The higher the melanin it's more likely to have (an) error," Williams added. "People are losing jobs and careers and Blacks are the ones suffering most for this."

> Woodford agreed with Williams and Swimmer that there is too much fallacy in using the results of a marijuana test when determining the future of Blacks and other naturally dark-skinned people.

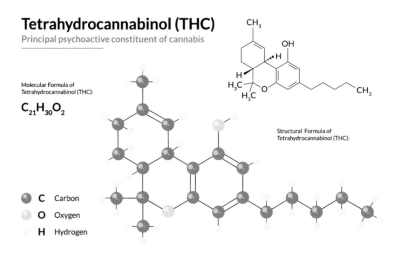

Tetrahydrocannabinol (THC)
Principal psychoactive constituent of cannabis

Molecular Formula of
Tetrahydrocannabinol (THC):

$C_{21}H_{30}O_2$

C   Carbon

O   Oxygen

H   Hydrogen

Structural Formula of
Tetrahydrocannabinol (THC):

Figure 45
THC molecular structure

A Secret System

As a scientist, I always like to do thorough research on a subject before speaking on it. After reading this Jet Magazine article I was intrigued to find out more about melanin and marijuana. What is it about THC that makes it bind to melanin? What other natural dietary substances have chemicals that resemble THC? Does marijuana have some type of affinity for melanin? It didn't take me long to find what I was looking for. I genuinely believe that the truth gravitates to those who seek it. It's like seeking the truth magnetically attracts it to you; especially when you are open to receiving it, soaking it up and absorbing it, like melanin does with light. Some say the truth hurts. But the truth is just the truth. How you feel about it doesn't change it. In fact, many believe the truth can be liberating! So those who are open to accepting it may experience a sense of liberation. I'm curious, have you ever had that feeling before? That feeling of release, that cleansing, purifying feeling which accompanies knowing the truth and letting go of all falsehood. Those fortunate enough to experience this feeling describe it as a natural high. A blissful state of living. This blissful state can actually be explained scientifically, and the science behind it has something to do with a secret system in your body that you've probably never heard of.

We've all heard of the cardiovascular system (consisting of your heart and lungs), the skeletal system (bones, joints, ligaments and tendons), muscular system (muscles and fascia) and the nervous system (brain, spinal cord and peripheral nerves). All of these systems are very important to how you function, because each one of them governs some aspect of your internal biological makeup. However, the secret system I'm about to reveal to you, governs them all! It is undoubtedly the most powerful system in the

159

body, especially when it comes to relieving pain and inflammation. And this just might be the first time you've ever heard of it, even if you've studied science at a very high level. It is located in the brain and in immune cells everywhere in the body. And... the most mind-blowing part of this system is that it has something to do with marijuana. Or should I say... cannabis (the original name). It is called the **endocannabinoid** system. Note the spelling. ENDOCANNABINOID (pronounced en-do-canna-bi-noid). In science, the prefix *endo-* means "*inside*" and the suffix *-oid* means "*resembling*" or "*like*". So, there's a secret system inside of you that resembles or acts like cannabis. Now why would you have a secret system inside of you that resembles or acts like cannabis? Read on... and prepare to be blown away!

ENDOCANNABINOID AND BODY SYSTEMS

Figure 46
ECS regulates all other systems

The Endocannabinoid System (ECS)

The endocannabinoid system, or ECS for short, is a biochemical communication system composed of two main endocannabinoids, anandamide and 2-arachidonoylglycerol (2-AG). These endocannabinoids are responsible for your body experiencing pleasure and removing pain. They bind to cannabinoid receptors in the brain and peripheral nervous system to carry out the daunting task of keeping the internal environment in a state of operative balance known as homeostasis, regardless of how the external environment fluctuates. As the name suggests, cannabinoid receptors receive cannabinoids, which are biochemical compounds found in cannabis. Two primary cannabinoid receptors have been identified: CB1 and CB2. CB1 receptors are found predominantly in the central nervous system (brain and spinal cord), whilst CB2 receptors are found in the peripheral nervous system,

160

digestive system and **melanocytes**. This secret system was actually discovered by accident in the early 90's by researchers studying the effects of THC, the main cannabinoid associated with marijuana. They found that THC was binding to these unknown receptors in the brain, causing neural activation of the mind and body. These unknown receptors were subsequently given the name CB1 and later more receptors in the body were discovered, so they were called CB2. Here's where the story gets real interesting.

Perplexed as to why the body would have receptors for cannabis compounds, the researchers later discovered that the human brain produces its own type of THC called anandamide. They found that this internal cannabinoid (endogenous cannabinoid) had a nearly identical chemical structure to THC and was capable of producing similar mind-altering effects. Anandamide is named after Ananda, the Sanskrit word for joy, 'divine happiness' or 'bliss,' which is why it is commonly known as "the bliss molecule." This internal cannabinoid can give you the feeling of being high, naturally. When anandamide binds to cannabinoid receptors in the brain and body, it stimulates a sense of ecstasy, happiness and mental wellbeing. These are the exact same receptors that THC bind to during the act of smoking marijuana. Furthermore, when THC binds to the endocannabinoid receptors it becomes a supreme pain reliever. One would assume that perhaps anandamide has the same effect. Now, I'm not one to smoke marijuana, but I've been around enough smokers in my life to know what they're feeling and how cannabis affects them. Some of them say they feel relaxed, calm, contemplative and introspective. Whilst others have reported feelings of elation, energy, and euphoria. These feelings are often followed by giggles, enjoyment and "the munchies". Either way, cannabis is used worldwide by people of all colours for predominantly the same reason: To feel good and be free of pain. This is the reason why CBD (cannabidiol), another cannabinoid found in the cannabis plant, is so popular with people seeking pain-relief.

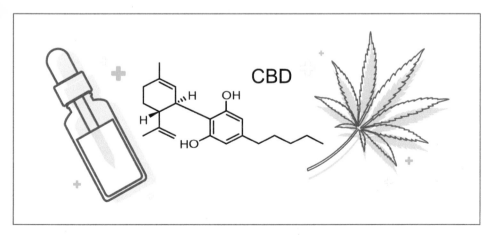

Figure 47
CBD oil supplementation

161

Benefits of CBD

CBD is known to be a very powerful pain reliever due to its interactions with the ECS. Numerous studies from around the world clearly show CBD's effectiveness at reducing pain and inflammation related to acute and chronic conditions like arthritis. One study, from researchers at Imperial College London, showed that CBD reduced inflammation in mice by fifty percent [106]. Another study, from Hebrew University, found that CBD prevented the onset of diabetes in mice [107]. CBD has also been found to reduce seizures and associated behavioural comorbidities in a range of animal seizure and epilepsy models [107]. One may read this and think to themselves, "Yeah, but that's in mice. What about human trials?" Well, the use of cannabis sativa plant in treating seizures in humans has been known since ancient times [108]. However, clinical trials prior to two years ago have shown little to no significant effects of cannabis in reducing seizures. These trials seem to be underpowered, with a sample size less than 15. In contrast, more recent studies that have included over 100 participants showed that CBD use resulted in a significant reduction in seizure frequency [108]. CBD is not the only cannabinoid that has shown to be effective against seizures, pain and inflammation.

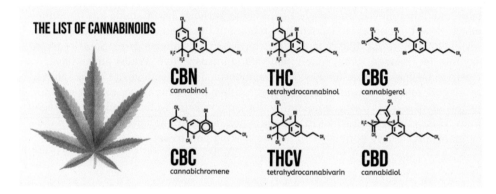

Figure 48
List of Phytocannabinoids

At least 113 distinct cannabinoids have been isolated from the cannabis plant. Of which, THC and CBD have both shown positive results in pain-relief trials, with the latter considered safer and more effective in treating seizures. In contrast to THC, CBD lacks psychoactive properties, does not produce euphoric or intrusive side effects, and is largely devoid of abuse liability [109]. In other words, it is widely considered to be safe to use in recommended doses. Can you imagine if the code of silence around cannabis was lifted? Imagine, just for one moment, a world where using a plant to aid in pain-relief was not demonized and sanctioned. A world where those who were suffering from chronic pain could turn to mother nature without the fear of being criminalised and locked up. I'll let you ponder that thought in your own time. Now let's bring this full circle back round to melanin. Follow me whilst I connect the dots...

162

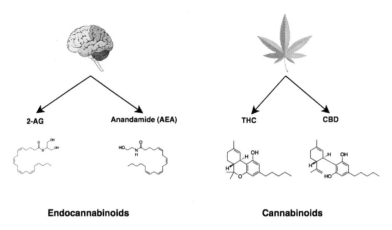

Endocannabinoids   Cannabinoids

Figure 49
Endocannabinoids vs Phytocannabinoids

Foods For ECS

According to Dr. Jewel Poolkrum, melanin shows extreme affinity for binding with fatty type compounds. In her eye-opening book *Vitamins & Minerals from A to Z* (1993), she mentions that the more melanin-dominant the individual is, the greater the affinity they have to retain excess fat in the body or store fats taken in from the diet. This could potentially be a bad thing if you're consuming the type of fats known to contribute to obesity and heart disease; like saturated animal fats found in beef, pork, chicken, lamb, turkey, sausages, processed meats, butter, cheese, lard and oils such as palm oil, margarine, corn oil, and sunflower oil. But if you are consuming healthy fats, especially those found in foods high in polyunsaturated fatty acids (PUFAs), then this could be beneficial to your ECS. PUFAs, like omega-6 and omega-3, are precursors of endocannabinoids [110]. So, utilising melanin's ability to bind to these types of fats could, in fact, boost the production of endocannabinoids, leading to the natural high associated with anandamide. There are many food sources containing PUFAs but studies have shown that one of the healthiest sources is algae or sea vegetables [68,111]. Algae usually comes in distinct colours including red algae like Chondrus Crispus (thank you Dr. Sebi), brown algae (Kelp), and green algae like Chlorella. Now, I know what you're thinking.. "Urgh, I hate the taste of sea vegetables!" Well, fear not! As there are some other sources you could try that might boost the ECS. There are some examples in the *FOODS FOR MELANIN* chapter that you may find helpful, under the omega-3 list. Additionally, foods like avocados and avocado oil have a healthy amount of PUFA content. Black cumin seeds and black seed oil are both high in essential PUFA's. This may be the reason why black seed oil is traditionally known to cure many diseases, dating back to ancient times. Hemp seeds and hemp oil have been shown to be one of the best natural dietary sources of THC. It might surprise you to know that hemp plants and marijuana plants are both the same species. Legally, hemp is defined as a cannabis plant that contains 0.3 percent or less THC, while marijuana is a cannabis plant that contains more than 0.3 percent THC. The very popular CBD oil can be derived from both hemp and

163

marijuana plants. Consuming these phytocannabinoids (phyto meaning plant) could potentially enhance the effect of your endocannabinoids. Non-cannabis sources that could help include chia seeds, flax seeds and walnuts; which are all high in PUFA's, so your melanin will bind to these quickly. Another non-cannabis alternative is surprisingly chocolate! Yes, go on smile. I smiled too when I found this out for the very first time. Chocolate is thought to contain both anandamide and compounds that slow its breakdown. This could explain the immediate feeling of bliss and happiness that chocolate lovers experience after eating their favourite dark treat. Maybe this is the reason why chocolate is also considered the number one food craving. The content of cannabinoid-like compounds in chocolate varies widely and is highest in raw dark chocolate and raw cacao.

Phytocannabinoids

Consuming the cannabinoids found in plants (phytocannabinoids) can enhance your ECS. However, please do not take this information the wrong way. The consumption of phytocannabinoids would be through the use of oils and / or supplements and not through smoking weed. The message to take away from this chapter is not that "weed is good for you and we should all start smoking it." No, the message is: There are natural ways to boost your ECS without having to light up a spliff. In fact, relying on marijuana for your 'highs' could have an adverse effect on the ECS over time. Simply because the THC would be binding to the same receptor site that anandamide should be binding to. Imagine a lock and key scenario, with the key being the cannabinoid and the lock being the receptor. If the THC key is inserted into the anandamide receptor lock, there's no use for the anandamide key, thus the body stops producing it. So, instead of the body producing its own internal keys to these cannabinoid receptor locks, it now has to rely on external keys. That's what phytocannabinoids are: external keys to your internal cannabinoid locks. Some may query then, why we need these external keys at all, if we have our own keys? In other words, why do any of us need phytocannabinoids if our body makes endocannabinoids? Well, because the body is constantly being overwhelmed and overloaded with toxins from the environment, chemicals,

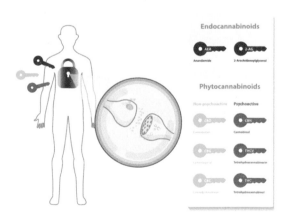

THE ENDOCANNABINOID SYSTEM

Figure 50
ECS keys

inflammatory foods, stress, pain and disease. These things all impact the ECS making it more and more difficult for your internal keys (like anandamide) to do their job. So a little help from the external keys (like CBD) may sometimes be warranted and necessary; in the form of supplementation. The same way if someone was low on Vitamin D their doctor may advise them to take a Vitamin D supplement to help top up their levels. It's the same logic. The difference between Vitamin D supplementation and cannabinoid supplementation however, is that phytocannabinoids have been scientifically proven to enhance the ECS. To this day, there's still no evidence to suggest that Vitamin D supplements enhance the "active form" of Soltriol. So supplementing with phytocannabinoids is more scientifically valid.

There are over 100 different types of phytocannabinoids found in the cannabis plant. THC and CBD are the stars of the show, but considering the many other cannabinoids found in cannabis your ECS has a wide variety of natural chemical compounds that could potentially enhance it. And it's not just the compounds that have a positive effective on human health. The cannabis plant also synthesises cannabinoid acids which act as the precursors to the phytocannabinoid compounds. Two acids in particular, cannabigerolic acid (CBGA) and cannabidiolic acid (CBDA), have been shown to be very effective at preventing the virus that causes COVID-19 from entering human cells [112]. In a report published by the *Journal of Natural Products* entitled, "Cannabinoids Block Cellular Entry of SARS-CoV-2 and the Emerging Variants," the researchers found that CBGA and CBDA can bind to the spike protein of SARS-CoV-2, the virus that causes COVID-19. By binding to the spike protein, these acids can prevent the virus from entering cells and causing infection, potentially offering new avenues to prevent and treat the disease. Both CBGA and CBDA are abundant in hemp and hemp extracts.

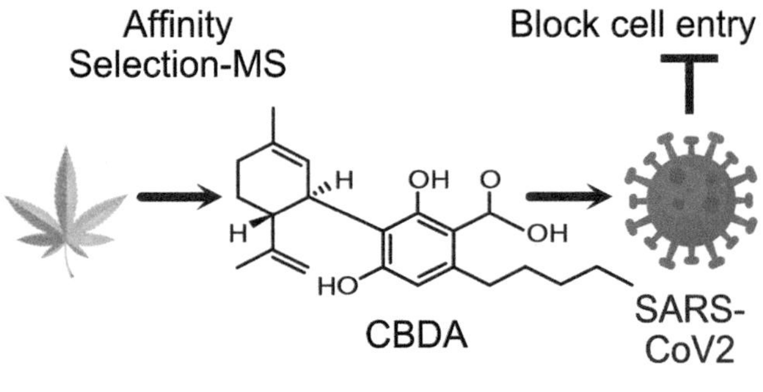

Figure 51
CBDA blocks entry to cell

Exercise and Endocannabinoids

So we've gone through some great food sources and supplements that could potentially boost your ECS. These could lead to reduced pain in the body and uplifting feelings of joy. Now, are there any activities that could help? Yes of course, and surprise surprise, they are things we really should be doing on a daily basis anyway. Exercise has been shown to boost the ECS, but it must be exercise that you enjoy! Exercise can sometimes be a stress on the body and chronic stress can have a detrimental effect on your health. If the exercise you are doing is very tedious or not enjoyable, it could actually deplete your endocannabinoid levels. Animal studies teach us that if you force yourself to exercise, your ECS will interpret the activity as stressful. But freely choosing and enjoying the same activity can have the opposite effect and increase endocannabinoid levels. Runners who experience a sense of euphoria whilst running, commonly known as "runner's high" may be tapping into this secret system unknowingly. The runner's high has been described subjectively as pure happiness, elation, a feeling of unity with one's self and/or nature, endless peacefulness, inner harmony, boundless energy, and a reduction in pain sensation [113]. Once believed to be the result of endorphins that work as analgesics and create feelings of euphoria, this idea has recently come under scrutiny [114,115]. It is now believed that the body releases anandamide to help cope with the prolonged stress and pain of vigorous or intense exercise. Simply socialising has also been shown to aid in the release of anandamide. One study found that rats in social isolation produced less endocannabinoids. In contrast, unrestricted social play increased functions of cannabinoid receptors, leading to more uptake. In other words, socialising and being around your own group of loved ones produces more endocannabinoids. Further studies have found that endocannabinoids increase immensely in response to singing and dancing. The overwhelming evidence suggests that just doing things you love will enhance the effects of the ECS. Why? Because doing things that you love stimulates feelings of pleasure. What many scientists and researchers are finally starting to realise is that these pleasurable feelings are due to anandamide's effect on the ECS.

Sex, Reproduction and Endocannabinoids

If feelings of pleasure are associated with the ECS, does that mean sexual feelings could be enhanced by this system too? Of course! There have been several studies published in the Journal of Sexual Medicine that show a direct connection between sexual arousal and endocannabinoids. One particular study revealed a significant relationship between endocannabinoid concentrations and female sexual arousal [116]. According to their findings, the endocannabinoid system is heavily involved in female sexual functioning. They found that within the female reproductive tract, endocannabinoid receptors are widespread. They are most dense in the uterus, but are also found in the fallopian tubes, ovaries, vagina and vulva. On a microscopic level, endocannabinoid receptors are located where they can exert control. They are associated with

- nerves where they mediate sensations
- immune cells where they control inflammation
- glands where they influence hormone secretion
- muscles where they facilitate energy usage

The results from this study suggest that the ECS is fully integrated into the sexual / reproductive tract, and thus plays a vital role in sexual pleasure, pregnancy and childbirth. Even post-childbirth the ECS is still very active inside the female's body. Studies show that both anandamide and 2-arachidonoylglycerol (2-AG) are present in breast milk, with 2-AG being more prevalent [117-119]. 2-AG appears to be very critical in keeping newborns alive, as it stimulates the suckling response and tongue muscles during breastfeeding. In other words, the endocannabinoid 2-AG is responsible for stimulating the newborns' appetite.

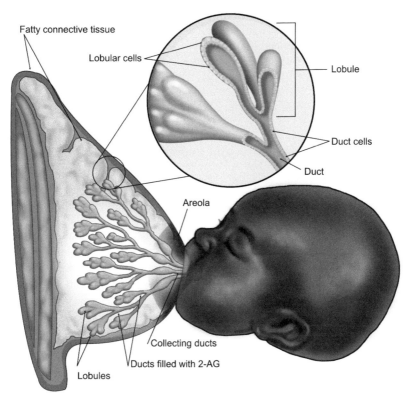

Figure 52
Endocannabinoid-Rich Breast Milk

The science community has known for years that the phytocannabinoid THC was linked with appetite stimulation (this is the reason why those who smoke cannabis experience "the munchies" afterwards). What's only now becoming clear is that the endocannabinoids within breast milk is what first prompts a baby's appetite. Without this prompt the baby would lose out on receiving all the essential nutrients in the mother's milk. The human body is hardwired to encourage behaviours—such as eating, exercising and sexual activity—that lead to pleasure, happiness and joy. So it should come as no surprise that all of these behaviours activate the release of endocannabinoids. Behaviours and activities that support health and the survival of the species are rewarded through powerful messages to the brain's pleasure-reward-memory circuits. You now know, from reading this book, that it's the ECS which is the driving force behind these messages, especially where sex and appetite is concerned. Aside from sexual activity, what other activities have been shown to enhance this powerful messaging system?

167

Here's a list of some other endocannabinoid enhancing activities:

- Yoga
- Tai Chi
- Meditation
- Massage Therapy
- Acupuncture

- Social Interactions
- Breathing Exercises
- Unstructured Play Time
- Osteopathic Manipulation
- Any voluntary and enjoyable exercise!

Melanogenesis and Endocannabinoids

To the astute truth seeker who still may not be convinced of melanin's direct connection to the ECS, recent research could prove to be persuasive. For the sake of clarity, let us now examine the true relationship between endocannabinoids and melanin. Studies show that endocannabinoids stimulate melanin synthesis and enhance tyrosinase gene expression and activity [120]. In other words, melanogenesis is enhanced by endocannabinoid activation. How is this possible? If you recall, in the *MELANOGENESIS* chapter of this book it was mentioned that the melanocyte stimulating hormone (MSH), by way of melatonin, stimulates melanin synthesis. So why then would the body need endocannabinoids for melanogenesis? In a research paper published by the Journal of Biological Chemistry called *Endocannabinoids Stimulate Human Melanogenesis via Type-1 Cannabinoid Receptor*, the authors detected the bliss molecule, anandamide, to be present inside human melanocytes [120]. Once activated, it stimulates melanogenesis by enhancing the activity of the enzyme responsible for melanin synthesis: Tyrosinase. It turns out, both MSH and anandamide can stimulate melanin synthesis by themselves. However, when combined the researchers reported a near 30% increase in tyrosinase activity. What's the best way to combine the two? Well, MSH relies on circadian rhythm; so making sure you're sleep-wake cycle is unaffected will help the body produce more MSH. As for anandamide, just doing the things you love can activate this powerful endocannabinoid, so activities that spark your joy and give you that wonderful feeling of enthusiasm will enhance anandamide activation. When I first discovered the "bliss molecule" I thought its properties sounded very similar to those associated with the neurotransmitter dopamine, found in large amounts in the substantia nigra. Dopamine was long thought to be the chemical responsible for our feelings of pleasure, but it seems like this may need to be revised. For many years, it was widely considered the "pleasure neurotransmitter" by the scientific community until scientists discovered that animals whose dopamine levels had been depleted by 99% still exhibited pleasurable reactions to sweet tastes [121]. Human trials even showed that administration of a dopamine blocker did not prevent participants from experiencing euphoria [122]. So where did these euphoric feelings come from? The endocannabinoid system might just hold the keys to many of life's mysteries.

Pause for a second and take a moment to digest what you've just read about. The relationship between melanin and cannabis is undeniable. You literally have a cannabis receptor system inside of you that, when activated correctly, can give you a natural high and relieve excruciating pain at the same time. Have you ever wondered why marijuana seems to be the drug of choice for many eumelanin-dominant individuals worldwide? Have you ever wondered why the media likes to publicly embarrass eumelanin athletes when they've (apparently) failed a drug test? Have you ever wondered why so many black men are incarcerated for marijuana offenses? Especially when you consider that the use of marijuana for both recreational and medicinal purposes has been legalized in nearly all states in America [123]. Logically speaking, worldwide legalization will undoubtedly rise in the coming years as the industry grows exponentially. According to a forecast report by Grand View Research, Inc., the rapid increase in legalization has put the legal marijuana market on track to be worth $70.6 billion globally by 2028.

So whilst the overall legal cannabis industry is booming, making large profits year after year, young black men are still given harsh penalties for possession. It's a head-scratching reality we find ourselves in at the moment. Some people are allowed to sell cannabis (and cannabis products) legally, whilst others get treated like criminals and thrown in jail. A report by the ACLU found that black people were four times more likely than whites to be arrested for marijuana possession; even though both groups consume marijuana at about the same rate [124]. Access into the legal cannabis market seems to show the same sort of bias. In 2017, 91% of marijuana business owners in the U.S. were white, 5.7% were Hispanic, 4.3% were Black and 2.4% were Asian [125]. Even the UK is seeing a boom in business owners, yet very few are Black. Who is really profiting from this new lucrative cannabis market? The Centre for Medicinal Cannabis claims the UK CBD market is currently worth £700 million and could hit £1 billion by 2025. Imagine if people knew the real science as to why cannabis was so effective and therefore so popular? Imagine if Black people understood why marijuana was made illegal in the first place and why even to this day, despite mass legalization black people are still criminalised and locked up for enjoying a plant. These are just a few things to think about as your mind connects the dots and starts putting two and two together.

One last time for emphasis: this chapter is NOT promoting or condoning the smoking of marijuana for eumelanin-dominant individuals to aid with any health conditions they may have. This chapter is not advocating for people to smoke weed to top up their melanin. However, the science around melanin, cannabis and endocannabinoids is clear. Melanin binds to the biochemical compounds in cannabis due to their similarities with internal biochemical compounds called endocannabinoids. Melanin binds strongly to THC due to its similarity with anandamide, the main endocannabinoid produced by the brain.

Why is the science community so silent on this? The code of silence around melanin and marijuana is deafening. We have a cannabis receptor system inside of us that, once activated, stimulates our melanin leading to feelings of bliss and joy. And the best part is, you don't need the cannabis plant to activate it. Simply doing things that you love can have the same effect as taking cannabis. So, let your hair down and dance to your favourite music, sing in the shower, meet up with friends and laugh until your sides hurt, play that sport you love to play or write that poetry you love to write. Make love to your partner and enjoy the pleasurable feelings of being loved; have babies and nurture the babies with endocannabinoid-rich breast milk. Creating these joyful experiences naturally is a much better way to enhance your ECS, rather than through the use of marijuana. Whatever your version of joy is—whether its yoga, running or being around family—will enhance your endocannabinoids. And if your version of joy happens to be sitting on the sofa, watching your favourite programme whilst bingeing on dark chocolate, at least you can now scientifically enjoy eating it and have fun burning the calories off afterwards. That's a win-win in my book.

Melanin Quiz 11 – Melanin and Marijuana

1 Due to its stable nature, melanin has the unique ability to bind to?
- **A.** Harmful drugs and chemical toxins
- **B.** Heavy metals
- **C.** Fatty type compounds (like PUFA's)
- **D.** All the above

2 What phytocannabinoid found in cannabis is the active ingredient responsible for marijuana's psychoactive side effects?
- **A.** CBD (Cannabidiol)
- **B.** CBG (Cannabigerol)
- **C.** THC (Tetrahydocannabidiol)
- **D.** TLC (Tender Loving Care)

3 According to the May (1986) edition of Jet Magazine, forensic scientists from Atlanta discovered that
- **A.** There is no affinity between melanin and marijuana
- **B.** The urine tests used for marijuana are 100% accurate
- **C.** Melanin blocks marijuana absorption
- **D.** Melanin actually soaks up chemical compounds similar to tetrahydrocannabinol (THC)

4 What is the Endocannabinoid System (ECS)?
- **A.** It's a biochemical communication system that only weed smokers can benefit from
- **B.** It's a biochemical communication system composed of two main endocannabinoids: anandamide and 2-AG
- **C.** It's a plant chemical communication system composed of two main phytocannabinoids: THC and CBD
- **D.** It doesn't exist

5 What is anandamide commonly known as?
- **A.** The "bliss" molecule
- **B.** The "high" molecule
- **C.** The "spiritual" molecule
- **D.** The "marijuana" molecule

6 **Why are PUFA's like Omega 6 and Omega 3 important for the endocannabinoid system?**
   A.   They are the precursors of endocannabinoids
   B.   Melanin shows extreme affinity to bind to them
   C.   They boost the production of endocannabinoids
   D.   All the above

7 **Scientists have now discovered that it is the release of _____ which causes the "runner's high," a sense of euphoria experienced whilst running**
   A.   Anandamide
   B.   Endophins
   C.   Dopamine
   D.   Oxytocin

8 **Which of the following has been found to contain anandamide?**
   A.   White Chocolate
   B.   Dark Chocolate
   C.   Fried Chicken
   D.   Vegan Burgers

9 **2-AG has been shown to be very critical in keeping newborns alive because...**
   A.   it stimulates the suckling response
   B.   it stimulates the tongue muscles during breastfeeding
   C.   it stimulates the newborns appetite
   D.   All the above

10 **What type of activities has been shown to activate the release of endocannabinoids?**
   A.   Meditation
   B.   Massage Therapy
   C.   Making Love
   D.   All the above

CHAPTER TWELVE

PSEUDOSCIENCE OF MELANIN

PSEUDOSCIENCE OF MELANIN

The word pseudoscience is derived from the Greek word pseudo meaning false and the English word science, from the Latin word scientia, meaning "knowledge." This is a term that gets thrown around a lot when melanin is the main focus of discussion. In recent years, many great melanin scholars have been labelled with this term. Dr. Llaila Afrika's work was once labelled as pseudoscience, as was Dr. Leonard Jeffries and Dr. Naim Akbar to name a few. What's very interesting to note about the published work these scholars have left behind is that their source of information about what melanin does and how it works is predominantly from published scientific papers written by European scientists. Despite this fact, these scholars (and many more like them) are commonly referred to as "Melanin Theorists" as a way of discrediting their work. Do a quick search online and you'll find that the term "Melanin Theory" is closely associated with pseudoscience. It seems strange to label people who talk about melanin as 'melanin theorists' or 'pseudo' when their source of information is from peer reviewed papers and reputable scientists from all over the world, like Dr. Frank Barr et al for example. In 1983, Dr. Frank Barr and his colleagues published the very revealing paper entitled: *Melanin: the organising molecule.* In this paper, they emphasise early and often melanin's crucial organisational role within living systems:

"The fact that melanin is the most primitive and universal pigment in living organisms, present since the inception of life, would make its hypothesized organizational role particularly important. In searching for a basic organizational molecule, it would make sense to identify a primitive polymer which appears early in evolutionary process and which subsequently develops an impressive functional repertoire. As this paper will show, melanin / neuromelanin presents itself as a singular candidate for such a role."

This paper even touched on the forbidden notion that melanin exists in all living cells in the human body. A notion that no one in the scientific community dares to suggest today, let alone explore and research to see if it's true.

"While this paper mainly discusses the observable properties of detectable cellular melanin, the possibility that melanin is significantly present in all cells and in all living organisms deserves careful attention. In those few "amelanotic" organisms where melanin's presence is still unclear, several possible explanations for its non-detection may be offered. First, on some occasions, when melanin has been repeatedly said to be totally absent, different techniques for detection have found it to be present in abundance."

This paper is one of the most extensive pieces of scientific research ever published about the biological importance of melanin. After this came out there should've been no more confusion around what melanin does, how it's formed or where it's located within the human body. It was all laid out thoroughly, in meticulous detail in this scientific paper from 1983 (with over 700 references!!!). However, many scientists at the time decided to hide, downplay or disregard its findings and even question the authors' motives for researching melanin. For some strange reason many scientists, to this day, have an issue with scientific research on melanin being made freely available to the public. Why do you think that is? For some reason, when melanin is discussed in a very positive way, you'll find naysayers, doubters and detractors come out of the woodwork to discredit, defame and disprove its importance to life and all living organisms. Have you noticed this or is it just me? Have you noticed how those who dare to mention melanin in a positive light are portrayed? Those individuals who have attempted to teach the masses about the science of melanin get labelled "pseudo," "afrocentric" or "melanists." This is how the science community gets away with name-calling without it seeming childish or immature. Instead of investigating what these "melanists" are actually saying about melanin and seeing if there's any truth to it, they name-call and point fingers like children do in school. Nowhere is this more evident than in a published paper from 1993 entitled: *Melanin, Afrocentricity, and Pseudoscience* by Bernard R. Ortiz de Montellano [126].

Melanists and Afrocentricity

In this paper, Ortiz de Montellano tries his very best to refute and disprove what some of the most knowledgeable black scholars have said about melanin. He takes aim at scholars like Dr. Richard King, Dr Jawanza Kunjufu, Dr. Wade Nobles, Naim Akbar, Anthony T. Browder, Carol Barnes and even Dr. Frances Cress Welsing (one of the greatest black scholars ever). Dr. Welsing, who herself was subject to endless name-calling whilst she was alive (they called her a black supremacist), once said that the genius black inventor Dr. George Washington Carver was able to talk to plants due to the melanin in his internal nervous system. She says in *The Isis Papers* that Carver "used or was able to use his black melanin pigment to decode the energy emanations from plants. Thus, they did talk to him" (Welsing, 1987). This was immensely refuted by Ortiz de Montellano:

> *"There is no correlation between skin pigmentation and neuromelanin. There is no reason to believe that Carver had any more neuromelanin than any white or black man his age. There is no scientific evidence for the existence of extra sensory perception or for communication between plants and people."*

In other words, how dare you try to attribute someone's greatness to their melanin! There's no way a man can communicate with a plant!! That's my interpretation of what's being said here anyway. I find myself having to do this often when reading scientific papers; decipher and interpret what they're *actually* saying, because the language used in these papers is so confusing to understand (especially when they are talking about melanin). The language is almost encrypted in the way it is written. It's damn near impossible to find one published paper, just one, out of the hundreds that are out there, without some type of confusing coded language thrown in there to dazzle you and make your head spin. Even when scientists perform experiments on melanin in a laboratory and the results conclusively show what it can do, they still publish the paper describing melanin's functions with ambiguous words like "*maybe,*" "*possibly,*" and "*likely.*" In other words, they always describe melanin's functions in terms of it being a theory and not a fact. For example, in the Barr et al. paper they say it is likely that melanin has an important role in the functioning of the central nervous system. Likely?! It's not likely at all. It's an absolute fact! Neuromelanin literally controls your central nervous system. Without it you'd suffer from all types of neurodegenerative diseases, of which Parkinson's disease being the most reported. But for some strange reason, instead of being direct and clear, they use words that leave a sense of doubt and uncertainty about what melanin can actually do. Although Ortiz de Montellano's paper was written to refute Barr's findings on melanin, he made sure to applaud Barr on his use of this type of loose language:

> To his credit, Barr makes liberal use of words like "perhaps," "possibly," "hypothetically," and "may prove to be." None of these qualifiers appear in the work of the melanists.

Why do you think he encourages this type of language? It's like he was saying "Attaboy, that's how you talk about melanin" to Barr. This type of language keeps melanin under the 'theory' umbrella, when there's more than enough evidence to state confidently the facts. It goes back to what I was saying about how science is taught to children. It's taught in a very confusing, convoluted way due to the language used. Can you imagine if we taught children maths in the same way that we teach children science?

> **Teacher:** "Ok settle down class, settle down. Today I am going to teach you the theory of 2+2.

> **Little Johnny:** "What's that sir?!"

> **Teacher:** "Well, the theory of 2+2 speculates that if you were to put two and two together, it's likely the answer might be 4. Hypothetically speaking, perhaps it could possibly, potentially be 4. We're not entirely sure though. It may prove to be. Who knows? Maybe, maybe not"

> **Johnny:** "Sir, I'm confused"

> **Teacher:** "No need to be confused Johnny it's just a theory"

In science, there seems to be many theories and few facts. For example, you have the famous theory of relativity by Albert Einstein. This theory explains the way gravity works in space and time. It's a theory that has now come under scrutiny due to the ever-expanding "dark universe" [79]. There's also the big bang theory, which Albert Einstein didn't believe in by the way (but that's neither here nor there). Another famous theory is the quantum theory, made famous by Max Planck, the scientist who pioneered the term Blackbody Radiation. Then there's the germ theory of disease (a popular one these days), and let's not forget the theory of evolution as well. So many theories. Where are the facts? All of these scientific theories create confusion. This is why I pride myself on teaching science in a simplified way. So whether I'm in a school teaching children about how the body works, or in a university lecture hall teaching young adults about how the brain works, I always try to keep things super simple.

176

Research and References

Many years ago, when I first started to teach people about melanin, I'd often get the odd one or two students interrupt the class just to say something like, "What's your source of information? I don't believe this!" or "Where are you getting your evidence from? Where's your proof?" I'd always respond politely with my source of information, including references and recommendations for further reading. Sometimes, weeks after making a recommendation I'd ask them, "Did you read that book I recommended about melanin?" Nine times out of ten, guess what they would say? err...No! It made me wonder why someone would go out of their way to disrupt the class asking for references and proof, and then not research the references or search for the proof themselves. We live in the information age (also known as the Computer Age, Digital Age or New Media Age) where anything you wanted to know about the universe, you could find at the tip of your fingers in seconds. Gone are the days where you had to enrol yourself into a top university to get the highest quality information about science. Not too long ago, this was the only way to learn about subjects like neurology or biochemistry. Nowadays, in this information age, you can learn about whatever you like, at the touch of a button. There is no middle man between you and knowledge. Seek and you shall find. The journey of knowledge, truth and education never ends. The universe should be your university, as it is mine. There is always something new to learn and discover. I myself am still learning (Thank you, Mr Fuller).

The more I know, the more I realise I don't know. And no human walking this Earth is error-free. As a human being, I am highly flawed and fallible, just as much as you are. I am not perfect, and I don't pretend to be. Every human is prone to error. So who knows, *maybe* there are some errors in this book that I am unaware of. *Possibly* so, my melanin research could be wrong. This *may prove to be* the case. *Perhaps* I might be the next one they call "*pseudo*", "*afrocentric*" or a "*melanist*". It is *likely* that they will refute the findings in this book and label it misinformation or scientific illiteracy. How could anything I say about melanin be accurate when I'm not even a "real" scientist (*hypothetically*, this may be their conjecture). Nevertheless, I continue to live by my own definition of science, which is: Logic, backed up by evidence. What's 2+2? This is just simple logic, common sense. You know the answer instinctively, without external validation. If I was to say to you, "But what's your source? I don't believe you! Where are you getting your evidence from?!" you might look at me in a perplexed way. Because you know deep down, **YOU** are the source! You are the evidence! The answer lies within you. You've always had the answer, even before the question was posed to you. Before someone showed you the truth, you knew it, because you are the truth!

The Evidence is You!

"What's 2+2? Prove it!" You could literally show me the answer without telling me, it doesn't take much to prove it. You could show me that 2+2 = 4 using your own fingers or even using mine. You could show me that 2+2 = 4 by using your arms and your legs, or your ears and your eyes. What you don't need to show me however, is a hundred and twenty six scientific references proving that 2+2 = 4. You don't need to reference anyone, but yourself; because you are the source, you are the evidence, you are the proof, you are the truth. I wonder if you're absorbing what I'm saying.

177

There's nothing 'pseudo' about what you see when you look in the mirror. You don't need someone in a white coat studying HeLa cells in a petri dish to tell you the truth about who YOU are. Look internally. The conscious human being has only two ways to turn to understand their existence and therefore their purpose on this planet; outward towards the physical world for answers or inward towards the universal self where all the answers dwell. Tap into the science within; that universal logic that is within all of us. That calm inner voice which intuitively knows itself and knows how the human body works already. Yeah... tap into that source... and see if you don't start putting two and two together!

Science of Self

I've been teaching science for over 15 years in schools, colleges and universities. It really amazes me when I think about what I do for a living, considering how much I hated science growing up. I look back and wonder why. Why on Earth did I hate it so much? Maybe it's because the teachers never made it simple. Maybe it's because they used scientific jargon I didn't understand. Maybe it's because I couldn't see the point of what they were teaching me. "How does this relate to me and my life? Why do I need to know this? Please explain to me how knowing this will help me in the future?" I never did get the answers to my questions, so I left school confused about the world and how I fit into it. Learning about melanin in my later years ignited a new found passion for science that I never thought existed. I now realise the mistakes that most science teachers make when teaching the subject to their students. They teach science as if it's separate from self. For example, in your physics class they'll teach you about Electricity and Electromagnetism but won't relate this to your electromagnetic body. In your biology class they'll teach you how cells form and organise themselves, and how this affects genetics; but won't teach you about melanin's role in forming and organising every single one of your cells during embryogenesis. In your chemistry class they'll teach you about the elements that appear on the periodic table, like carbon and gold, but won't tell you that the ancient study of chemistry was called alchemy, and alchemy originally means "The Black Land." This comes from Ancient Kemet, which was the original name of Egypt. The ancient Egyptian word KM (pronounced in English as Khem) means black (KM = Khem = Chem). The suffix -istry means *"the study of or knowledge about that specific field."* So when they say they are studying "**chem**"istry just think about what they are really studying. YOU! You are science. When you study science, you are studying yourself!

You are physics
You are biology
You are chemistry

YOU... ARE... SCIENCE!

On Earth

Why **on Earth** would you need hundreds of scientific papers proving that the sun charges up your melanin like a battery, when you could just go outside in the sun and see how you feel?

Why **on Earth** would you need proof that the endocannabinoid system stimulates your melanin leading to feelings of bliss and joy when you know doing things you love gets you "high," naturally!

Why **on Earth** do you need a scientist to tell you that the melanin in your ears *and* your skin absorbs low bass frequencies and converts low bass sounds into electrical impulses, when you know you don't just hear music, you feel it!

Why **on Earth** would you need a group of European scientists to prove that the black substance in your brain called Substantia Nigra controls motor activity, leading to smooth coordinated movements, when you know you got rhythm! And that rhythm keeps you in alignment with the universe.

You already know the truth and that's why this book is resonating with you. It's teaching you about you. And there's no better subject -***On Earth***- to learn about.

Science is simple! It's just that you've been taught it in a confusing way. And there's only one of two reasons why:

(i) Either the person teaching you science doesn't understand the subject well enough...
(ii) Or they do, they just don't want you to understand it.

I'll let you put two and two together on that one.

My name is Leon Marshall, and that concludes the end of this book.

Thank you.

REFERENCES

1. Barr, F.E. (1983) Melanin: the organizing molecule. Med Hypotheses. 1983 May;11(1):1-139. doi: 10.1016/0306-9877(83)90122-6.

2. F. Solano. Melanins: Skin Pigments and Much More—Types, Structural Models, Biological Functions, and Formation Routes. Hindawi Publishing Corporation. New Journal of Science, Volume 2014, Article ID 498276, 28 pages, http://dx.doi.org/10.1155/2014/498276

3. Tahseen H Nasti, Laura Timares., MC1R, eumelanin and pheomelanin: their role in determining their susceptibility to skin cancer https://pubmed.ncbi.nlm.nih.gov/25155575/

4. Ancans J, Tobin DJ, Hoogduijn MJ, Smit NP, Wakamatsu K, Thody AJ, et al. Melanosomal pH controls rate of melanogenesis, eumelanin/phaeomelanin ratio and melanosome maturation in melanocytes and melanoma cells. Exp Cell Res. 2001;268:26–35.

5. Ito S, Wakamatsu K. Diversity of human hair pigmentation as studied by chemical analysis of eumelanin and pheomelanin. J Eur Acad Dermatol Venereol. 2011;25:1369–80.

6. Rees J. Plenty new under the sun. J Invest Dermatol. 2006;126:1691–2.

7. Rees JL. The melanocortin 1 receptor (MC1R): More than just red hair. Pigment Cell Res. 2000;13:135–40.

8. Abdel-Malek Z., Suzuki I., Tada A., Im S., Akcali C. The melanocortin-1 receptor and human pigmentation. Ann. N. Y. Acad. Sci. 1999;885:117–133.

9. Abdel-Malek Z., Scott M.C., Suzuki I., Tada A., Im S., Lamoreux L., Ito S., Barsh G., Hearing V.J. The melanocortin-1 receptor is a key regulator of human cutaneous pigmentation. Pigm. Cell Res. 2000;13:156–162.

10. Abdel-Malek Z.A., Knittel J., Kadekaro A.L., Swope V.B., Starner R. The melanocortin 1 receptor and the UV response of human melanocytes–A shift in paradigm. Photochem. Photobiol. 2008;84:501–508.

11. Kenny EE, Timpson NJ, Sikora M, Yee MC, Moreno-Estrada A, Eng C, et al. Melanesian blond hair is caused by an amino acid change in TYRP1. Science. 2012;336:554.

12. Simon JD, Peles D, Wakamatsu K, Ito S. Current challenges in understanding melanogenesis: bridging chemistry, biological control, morphology, and function. Pigment cell & melanoma research. 2009;22:563–579

13. Norgren R, Hajnal A, Mungarndee SS. Gustatory reward and the nucleus accumbens. Physiol Behav. 2006;89:531–535.

14. https://www.sciencedirect.com/topics/medicine-and-dentistry/parabrachial-nucleus

15. Ancans J, Tobin DJ, Hoogduijn MJ, Smit NP, Wakamatsu K, Thody AJ, et al. Melanosomal pH controls rate of melanogenesis, eumelanin/phaeomelanin ratio and melanosome maturation in melanocytes and melanoma cells. Exp Cell Res. 2001;268:26–35.

16. Rabey JM, Hefti F (1990) Neuromelanin synthesis in rat and human substantia nigra. J Neural Transm Park Dis Dement Sect 2(1):1-14.

17. Stepień K, Dzierzega-Lecznar A, Tam I (2007) Rola neuromelaniny w chorobie Parkinsona--nowe koncepcje The role of neuromelanin in Parkinson's disease--new concepts. Wiad Lek 60(11-12): 563-9.

18. Tribl F, Asan E, Arzberger T, Tatschner T, Langenfeld E, et al. (2009) Identification of L-ferritin in neuromelanin granules of the human substantia nigra: A targeted proteomics approach. Molecular & Cellular Proteomics 8(8): 1832-1838.

19. Sasaki M, Shibata E, Tohyama K, Takahashi J, Otsuka K, et al. (2006) Neuromelanin magnetic resonance imaging of locus ceruleus and substantia nigra in Parkinson's disease. Neuroreport 17(11): 1215-1218.

20. Usunoff KG, Itzev DE, Ovtscharoff WA, Marani E (2002) Neuromelanin in the human brain: A review and atlas of pigmented cells in the substantia nigra. Archives of Physiology and Biochemistry 110 (4): 257-369.

21. Lillie RD (1957) Metal reduction reactions of the melanins: Histochemical studies. Journal of Histochemistry and Cytochemistry 5(4): 325-333.

22. Zecca L, Tampellini D, Gerlach M, Riederer P, Fariello RG, et al. (2001) Substantia nigraneuromelanin: Structure, synthesis, and molecular behaviour. Molecular Pathology 54 (6): 414-418.

23. Brash DE, Goncalves LCP, Bechara EJH (2018) Excited-State Medicine Working Group. Chemiexcitation and Its Implications for Disease. Trends Mol Med 24(6): 527-541.

181

24. Tolleson W.H. (2009) Melanin and Neuromelanin in the Nervous System. In: Binder M.D., Hirokawa N., Windhorst U. (eds) Encyclopedia of Neuroscience. Springer, Berlin, Heidelberg.

25. Jewel Pookrum, M.D., Ph.D., (1993) Vitamins & Minerals from A to Z. Ethno-Conscious Series

26. M Tachibana (2006) Sound needs sound melanocytes to be heard. Pigment Cell Res. 1999 Dec;12(6):344-54. doi: 10.1111/j.1600-0749.1999.tb00518.x.

27. Olszewski, J. and Baxter, D. (1954). Cytoarchitecture of the Human brain stem. Basel: S. Karger.

28. Kim SJ, Sung JY, Um JW, Hattori N, Mizuno Y, et al. (2003) Parkin Cleaves Intracellular -Synuclein Inclusions via the Activation of Calpain. Journal of Biological Chemistry 278 (43): 41890-41899.

29. J. M. Burns, J. E. Galvin, C. M. Roe, J. C. Morris, D. W. McKeel, (2005) The pathology of the substantia nigra in Alzheimer disease with extrapyramidal signs. DOI: https://doi.org/10.1212/01.WNL.0000158423.05224.7F

30. Mehler Mark F, Dominick P Purpura (2009) Autism, fever, epigenetics and the locus coeruleus. Brain Research Reviews 59 (2): 388-392.

31. Mouton PR, Pakkenberg B, Gundersen HJ, Price DL (1994) Absolute number and size of pigmented locus coeruleus neurons in young and aged individuals. J Chem Neuroanat 7(3): 185-90.

32. Ann C. Brown, Richard D. King, T. Owens Moore. WHY DARKNESS MATTERS: The Power of Melanin In The Brain (New and Expanded Edition) 2020 publication

33. https://www.theguardian.com/science/2016/jun/05/human-development-ivf-embryos-14-day-legal-limit-extend-inside-black-box

34. Nadine L. Wicks, Jason W. Chan, Julia A. Najera, Jonathan M. Ciriello, Elena Oancea. UVA Phototransduction Drives Early Melanin Synthesis in Human Melanocytes. Current Biology, 2011 DOI: 10.1016/j.cub.2011.09.047

35. Lerner, E. J., "Why Can't A Computer Be More Like A Brain?", High Technology, pp. 34-41. August, 1984

36. Alireza Bina, Starwood Audiology (2021) The Link Between Brain and Auditory System and Possible Role of Vestibular System in Hearing System as a Second Middle Ear and the Role of Melanocytes and/or Neuromelanin in this Process https://irispublishers.com/ann/pdf/ANN.MS.ID.000728.pdf

37. Ruth Gussen (1978) Round Window Niche Melanocytes and Webby Tissue. Possible collateral route of vascular and perilymph circulation Arch Otolaryngol 104(11): 662-668.

38. Lian Gelis, Nikolina Jovancevic, Sophie Veitinger, Bhubaneswar Mandal, Hans-Dieter Arndt, Eva M. Neuhaus, Hanns Hatt. Functional Characterization of the Odorant Receptor 51E2 in Human Melanocytes. Journal of Biological Chemistry, 2016; jbc.M116.734517 DOI: 10.1074/jbc.M116.734517

39. Ezgi Doğan Cömert, Burçe Ataç Mogol, Vural Gökmen (2020) Relationship between color and antioxidant capacity of fruits and vegetables. Current Research in Food Science, Volume 2, June 2020, Pages 1-10

40. https://www.healthline.com/nutrition/polyphenols#what-they-are

41. Feng Liu-Smith, Frank L Meyskens, (2016) Molecular mechanisms of flavonoids in melanin synthesis and the potential for the prevention and treatment of melanoma. DOI: 10.1002/mnfr.201500822

42. M. L. Anson, and A. E. Mirsky (1930) HEMOGLOBIN, THE HEME PIGMENTS, AND CELLULAR RESPIRATION. Journal of Physiological Reviews, 01 JUL 1930 https://doi.org/10.1152/physrev.1930.10.3.506

43. Aleksandar Godic, Borut Poljšak, Metka Adamic, Raja Dahmane (2014) The role of antioxidants in skin cancer prevention and treatment. DOI: 10.1155/2014/860479

44. Rostand SG. Ultraviolet light may contribute to geographic and racial blood pressure differences. Hypertension. 1997;30:150–6.

45. https://www.ncbi.nlm.nih.gov/pmc/articles/PMC3356951/

46. Clemens TL, Henderson SL, Adams JS, Holick MF. Increased skin pigment reduces the capacity of skin to synthesise vitamin D3. Lancet. 1982;1:74–6.

47. Anna Aulinas, MD, PhD. (2019) Physiology of the Pineal Gland and Melatonin. https://www.ncbi.nlm.nih.gov/books/NBK550972/

48. Arch Otolaryngol 104(11): 662-668. Konrad Kleszczynski, Tae-kang Kim, Bernadetta Bilska, Michal Sarna, Kerstin Steinbrink, Markus Böhm, Andrzej Slominski, (2019) Melatonin regulates melanin synthesis in human melanogenic cells

49. Ran Liu, Alan Fu, Aaron E Hoffman, Tongzhang Zheng & Yong Zhu (2013) Melatonin enhances DNA repair capacity possibly by affecting genes involved in DNA damage responsive pathways

50. Per O. Lundmark, Seithikurippu R. Pandi-Perumal, Venkartaramanujan Srinivasan, Daniel P. Cardinalia (2007) Role of melatonin in the eye and ocular dysfunctions. Cambridge University Press

51. Marina Green-Gomez; Rachel Moran; James Stringham; Cesar Hernández-Alcaraz; Kenny Mendoza-Herrera; J. Jans Fromow-Guerra; Alfonso Prado-Cabrero; John Nolan (2021) Environmental and Nutritional Determinants of Macular Pigment in a Mexican Population. Investigative Ophthalmology & Visual Science July 2021, Vol.62, 18. doi:https://doi.org/10.1167/iovs.62.9.18

52. Zhi-Chun Zhao, Ying Zhou, Gang Tan, and Juan Li (2018) Research progress about the effect and prevention of blue light on eyes. International Journal of Ophthalmology. 2018; 11(12): 1999–2003. Published online 2018 Dec 18. doi: 10.18240/ijo.2018.12.20

53. https://www.ofcom.org.uk/about-ofcom/latest/media/media-releases/2020/lockdown-leads-to-surge-in-tv-screen-time-and-streaming

54. Sung Hoon Lee, Il-Hong Bae, Eun-Soo Lee, Hyoung-June Kim, Jongsung Lee, Chang Seok Lee (2020) Glucose Exerts an Anti-Melanogenic Effect by Indirect Inactivation of Tyrosinase in Melanocytes and a Human Skin Equivalent. Int. J. Mol. Sci. 2020, 21(5), 1736; https://doi.org/10.3390/ijms21051736

55. Abdelali Lehraiki, Patricia Abbe, Michael Cerezo, Florian Rouaud, Claire Regazzetti, Bérengère Chignon-Sicard, Thierry Passeron, Corine Bertolotto, Robert Ballotti, Stéphane Rocchi (2014) Inhibition of melanogenesis by the antidiabetic metformin. DOI: 10.1038/jid.2014.202

56. Elisabeth S Belisle, Hee-Young Park (2014) Metformin: a potential drug to treat hyperpigmentation disorders. DOI: 10.1038/jid.2014.245

57. https://www.valisure.com/blog/valisure-news/valisure-detects-benzene-in-sunscreen/

58. https://www.valisure.com/blog/valisure-news/valisure-detects-benzene-in-hand-sanitizers/

59. https://www.dailymail.co.uk/health/article-6997513/Sunscreen-absorbed-blood-concentrations-419-TIMES-safe.html

60. https://www.independent.co.uk/news/science/scientists-discover-how-red-wine-miracle-ingredient-resveratrol-helps-us-stay-young-9940742.html

61. Catalina Alarcón de la Lastra, Isabel Villegas (2005) Resveratrol as an anti-inflammatory and anti-aging agent: mechanisms and clinical implications. DOI: 10.1002/mnfr.200500022

62. Abdur Rauf, Muhammad Imran, Masood Sadiq Butt, Muhammad Nadeem, Dennis G Peters, Mohammad S Mubarak (2018) Resveratrol as an anti-cancer agent: A review. DOI: 10.1080/10408398.2016.1263597

63. Aniruddha Sengupta, Ulrike F Lichti, Bradley A Carlson, Andrew O Ryscavage (2010) Selenoproteins Are Essential for Proper Keratinocyte Function and Skin Development PLoS ONE 5(8):e12249 DOI:10.1371/journal.pone.0012249

64. G F Combs Jr. (2001) Selenium in global food systems. DOI: 10.1079/bjn2000280

65. Fernando Zapata-Gonzalez, Felix Rueda, Jordi Petriz, Pere Domingo, Francesc Villarroya, Julieta Diaz-Delfin, Maria A de Madariaga, Joan C Domingo (2008) Human dendritic cell activities are modulated by the omega-3 fatty acid, docosahexaenoic acid, mainly through PPAR(gamma):RXR heterodimers: comparison with other polyunsaturated fatty acids. DOI: 10.1189/jlb.1007688

66. Philip C Calder (2006) n-3 polyunsaturated fatty acids, inflammation, and inflammatory diseases. DOI: 10.1093/ajcn/83.6.1505S

67. Janice K Kiecolt-Glaser, Martha A Belury, Rebecca Andridge, William B Malarkey, Ronald Glaser (2011) Omega-3 supplementation lowers inflammation and anxiety in medical students: a randomized controlled trial. DOI: 10.1016/j.bbi.2011.07.229

68. Mark L. Wells, Philippe Potin, James S. Craigie, John A. Raven, Sabeeha S. Merchant, Katherine E. Helliwell, Alison G. Smith, Mary Ellen Camire, and Susan H. Brawley (2017) Algae as nutritional and functional food sources: revisiting our understanding. DOI: 10.1007/s10811-016-0974-5

69. Fleurence J., Morancais M., Dumay J., Decottignies P., Turpin V., Munier M., Garcia-Bueno N., Jaouen P. (2012) What are the prospects for using seaweed in human nutrition and for marine animals raised through aquaculture? Trends Food Sci. Technol. 2012;27:57-61 doi: 10.1016/j.tifs.2012.03.004

70. Stephanie Watson (2020) How Long Does It Take to Digest Food? All About Digestion. Medically reviewed by Saurabh Sethi, M.D., MPH https://www.healthline.com/health/how-long-does-it-take-to-digest-food

71. Lars Alfredsson, Bruce K Armstrong, D Allan Butterfield, Rajiv Chowdhury, Frank R de Gruijl, Martin Feelisch, Cedric F Garland, Prue H Hart, David G Hoel, Ramune Jacobsen, Pelle G Lindqvist, David J Llewellyn, Henning Tiemeier, Richard B Weller, Antony R Young (2020) Insufficient Sun Exposure Has Become a Real Public Health Problem DOI: 10.3390/ijerph17145014

72. Donald B Parrish, Earl F Richter (2009) Determination of vitamin D in foods: a review https://doi.org/10.1080/10408397909527272

73. Bernardus Mostert, Karl J. P. Davy, Jeremy L. Ruggles, Ben J. Powell, Ian R. Gentle, and Paul Meredith (2009) Gaseous Adsorption in Melanins: Hydrophilic Biomacromolecules with High Electrical Conductivities. https://doi.org/10.1021/la901290f

74. https://www.dailymail.co.uk/sciencetech/article-9392641/Bill-Gates-wants-spray-millions-tonnes-CHALK-stratosphere.html

75. A general and quantitative discussion of intramolecular radiationless transitions is the subject of an article by M. Bixon and J. Jortner (J. Chem. Phys., 48 (2) 715-726 (1968))

76. Meredith, P.; Riesz, J. Radiative relaxation quantum yields for synthetic eumelanin. Photochem. Photobiol. 2004, 79, 211–216.

77. Nofsinger, J. B., S. E. Forest, and J. D. Simon. 1999. Explanation for the disparity among absorption and action spectra of eumelanin. J. Phys. Chem. 103:11428–11432

78. Li, W.; Patil, A.; Zhou, X.; Wang, Z.; Xiao, M.; Shawkey, M.D.; Gianneschi, N.C.; Dhinojwala, A. Characterization of broadband complex refractive index of synthetic melanin coatings and their changes after ultraviolet irradiation. Appl. Phys. Lett. 2020, 117, 203701.

79. https://science.nasa.gov/astrophysics/focus-areas/what-is-dark-energy

80. N. Kollias, "The spectroscopy of human melanin pigmentation," in Melanin: Its Role in Human Photoprotection, pp. 31-38, Valdenmar Publishing, 1995.

81. Marianna Ambrico, Paolo F Ambrico, Antonio Cardone, Teresa Ligonzo, Stefania R Cicco, Rosa Di Mundo, Vincenzo Augelli, Gianluca M Farinola Melanin layer on silicon: an attractive structure for a possible exploitation in bio-polymer based metal-insulator-silicon devices DOI: 10.1002/adma.201101358

82. https://news.northwestern.edu/stories/2020/07/new-biomaterial-could-shield-against-harmful-radiation-selenomelanin/

83. https://www.researchgate.net/publication/236893797_Energy_Production_the_Main_Role_of_Melanin_in_the_Mesencephalon

84. Tahseen H. Nasti, Laura Timares (2014) MC1R. Eumelanin and Pheomelanin: Their Role in Determining the Susceptibility to Skin Cancer. Photochemistry and Photobiology 91(1) https://doi.org/ 10.1111/php.12335

85. Sara Akerström, Mehrdad Mousavi-Jazi, Jonas Klingström, Mikael Leijon, Ake Lundkvist, Ali Mirazimi (2005) Nitric oxide inhibits the replication cycle of severe acute respiratory syndrome coronavirus. Journal of Virology. 2005 Feb;79(3):1966-9. doi: 10.1128/JVI.79.3.1966-1969.2005

86. Daniel D Bikle (2011) Vitamin D: an ancient hormone Exp Dermatol. 2011 Jan;20(1):7 – 13. DOI: 10.1111/j.1600-0625.2010.01202.x.

87. W. E. Stumpf (2012) Vitamin D and the scientific calcium dogma: understanding the 'Panacea' of the sun. European Journal of Clinical Nutrition DOI: 10.1038/ejcn.2012.78

88. Camille E. Powe, M.D., Michele K. Evans, M.D., Julia Wenger, M.P.H., Alan B. Zonderman, Ph.D., Anders H. Berg, M.D., Ph.D., Michael Nalls, Ph.D., Hector Tamez, M.D., M.P.H., Dongsheng Zhang, Ph.D., Ishir Bhan, M.D., M.P.H., S. Ananth Karumanchi, M.D., Neil R. Powe, M.D., M.P.H., M.B.A., and Ravi Thadhani, M.D., M.P.H. (2013) Vitamin D–Binding Protein and Vitamin D Status of Black Americans and White Americans. New England Journal of Medicine 2013. Nov 21; 369(21): 1991–2000. doi: 10.1056/NEJMoa1306357

89. Steven R. Cummings, MD; Douglas P. Kiel, MD; Dennis M. Black, PhD; (2016) Vitamin D Supplementation and Increased Risk of Falling: A Cautionary Tale of Vitamin Supplements Retold. JAMA Intern Med. 2016;176(2):171-172. doi:10.1001/jamainternmed.2015.7568

90. Michelle Y O'Connor, BS; Caroline K Thoreson, BS; Natalie L M Ramsey, BS; Madia Ricks, RN; and Anne E Sumner, MD; (2013) The Uncertain Significance of Low Vitamin D levels in African Descent Populations: A Review of the Bone and Cardiometabolic Literature. Prog Cardiovasc Dis. 2013 Nov-Dec; 56(3): 261–269. doi: 10.1016/j.pcad.2013.10.015

91. Geber, M. (1958) The psycho-motor development of African children in the first year, and the influence of maternal behaviour. The Journal of Social Psychology, 47, 185-195. https://doi.org/10.1080/00224545.1958.9919238

92. Janet E Kilbride, Michael C. Robbins, Philip L. Kilbride (1970) The Comparative Motor Development of Baganda, American White, and American Black Infants. American Anthropologist Vol.72(6):1422 – 1428 https://doi.org/10.1525/aa.1970.72.6.02a00160

93. Michaela Brenner, Vincent J Hearing (2007) The protective role of melanin against UV damage in human skin Photochem Photobiol May-Jun 2008;84(3):539-49. doi: 10.1111/j.1751-1097.2007.00226.x.

94. Chedekel MR. Photochemistry and photobiology of epidermal melanins. Photochem Photobiol. 1982;35:881–885.

95. Chedekel MR, Post PW, Deibel RM, Kalus M. Photodestruction of phaeomelanin. Photochem Photobiol. 1977;26:651–653.

96. Chedekel MR, Smith SK, Post PW, Pokora A, Vessell DL. Photodestruction of pheomelanin: role of oxygen. Proc Natl Acad Sci U S A. 1978;75:5395–5399.

97. Felix CC, Hyde JS, Sarna T, Sealy RC. Melanin photoreactions in aerated media: electron spin resonance evidence for production of superoxide and hydrogen peroxide. Biochem Biophys Res Commun. 1978;84:335–341.

98. Prota G. The chemistry of melanins and melanogenesis. Fortschr Chem Org Naturst. 1995;64:93–148.

99. Harsanyi ZP, Post PW, Brinkmann JP, Chedekel MR, Deibel RM. Mutagenicity of melanin from human red hair. Experientia. 1980;36:291–292.

100. Cesarini JP. Photo-induced events in the human melanocytic system: photoaggression and photoprotection. Pigment Cell Res. 1988;1:223–233.

101. https://worldpopulationreview.com/country-rankings/total-fertility-rate

102. https://sitn.hms.harvard.edu/flash/2020/vessels-for-collective-progress-the-use-of-hela-cells-in-covid-19-research/

103. https://www.sciencenews.org/article/coronavirus-covid19-vaccine-ethical-issues

104. https://zeenews.india.com/health/hela-cells-cells-of-a-black-woman-who-died-of-cancer-70-years-ago-still-saves-millions-of-lives-2403760

105. Ludovico Migliaccio, Paola Manini, Davide Altamura, Cinzia Giannini, Paolo Tassini, Maria Grazia Maglione, Carla Minarini and Alessandro Pezzella (2019) Evidence of Unprecedented High Electronic Conductivity in Mammalian Pigment Based Eumelanin Thin Films After Thermal Annealing in Vacuum Front. Chem., 26 March 2019 https://doi.org/10.3389/fchem.2019.00162 https://www.frontiersin.org/articles/10.3389/fchem.2019.00162/full

106. Zach Reichard (2012) "Cannabidiol (CBD): Fighting Inflammation & Aggressive Forms of Cancer," Medical Jane

107. Pabitra Hriday Patra, Melissa Barker-Haliski, H Steve White, Benjamin J Whalley, Sarah Glyn, Haramrit Sandhu, Nicholas Jones, Michael Bazelot, Claire M Williams, Alister James McNeish (2019) Cannabidiol reduces seizures and associated behavioral comorbidities in a range of animal seizure and epilepsy models. 2019 Feb;60(2):303-314. doi: 10.1111/epi.14629. Epub 2018 Dec 26.

108. Sidra Zaheer, Deepak Kumar, Muhammad T Khan, Pirthvi Raj Giyanwani, Fnu Kiran (2018) Epilepsy and Cannabis: A Literature Review. Cureus 2018 Sep 10;10(9):e3278. doi: 10.7759/cureus.3278.

109. Simona Lattanzi, Francesco Brigo, Eugen Trinka, Gaetano Zaccara, Claudia Cagnetti, Cinzia Del Giovane, Mauro Silvestrini (2018) Efficacy and Safety of Cannabidiol in Epilepsy: A Systematic Review and Meta-Analysis. 2018 Nov;78(17):1791-1804. doi: 10.1007/s40265-018-0992-5.

110. Josephine E Watson, Justin S Kim, Aditi Das (2019) Emerging class of omega-3 fatty acid endocannabinoids & their derivatives. Prostaglandins & Other Lipid Mediators. Volume 143, August 2019, 106337 DOI: 10.1016/j.prostaglandins.2019.106337

111. Kavya R, Aakanksha Sharma and Dr. Roshni Rao (2016) A comparative study of PUFAs in Algae and higher plants. Journal of Pharmacognosy and Phytochemistry 2017; 6(1): 74-82. P-ISSN: 2349-8234

112. Richard B van Breemen, Ruth N Muchiri, Timothy A Bates, Jules B Weinstein, Hans C Leier, Scotland Farley, Fikadu G Tafesse (2022) Cannabinoids Block Cellular Entry of SARS-CoV-2 and the Emerging Variants. Journal of Natural Products. 2022 Jan 10. doi: 10.1021/acs.jnatprod.1c00946.

113. A Dietrich, W F McDaniel (2020) Endocannabinoids and exercise. British Journal of Sports Medicine. http://dx.doi.org/10.1136/bjsm.2004.011718

114. Kolata G . (2002) Runners high? Endorphins? Fiction say some scientists. The NY Times. 2002 May :21.

115. Schlicht W . (1994) Sport und Primärprävention. Göttingen: Hogrefe, 1994

116. Carolin Klein, Matthew N Hill, Sabrina C H Chang, Cecilia J Hillard, Boris B Gorzalka (2012) Circulating endocannabinoid concentrations and sexual arousal in women. Journal of Sexual Medicine, 2012 Jun;9(6):1588-601. doi: 10.1111/j.1743-6109.2012.02708.x. Epub 2012 Mar 29.

117. Vincenzo Di Marzo, Nunzio Sepe, Luciano De Petrocellis, Alvin Berger, Gayle Crozier, Ester Fride & Raphael Mechoulam (1998) Trick or treat from food endocannabinoids? Nature 1998 Dec 17;396(6712):636-7. doi: 10.1038/25267.

118. Junfang Wu, Sandra Gouveia-Figueira, Magnus Domellöf, Angela M.Zivkovic, Malin L.Nording (2016) Oxylipins, endocannabinoids, and related compounds in human milk: Levels and effects of storage conditions. Prostaglandins & Other Lipid Mediators. Volume 122, January 2016, Pages 28-36

119. Igor Granta and B. Rael Cahn (2016) Cannabis and endocannabinoid modulators: Therapeutic promises and challenges. Clin Neurosci Res. 2005; 5(2-4): 185–199. doi: 10.1016/j.cnr.2005.08.015

120. Mariangela Pucci, Nicoletta Pasquariello, Natalia Battista, Monia Di Tommaso, Cinzia Rapino, Filomena Fezza, Michela Zuccolo, Roland Jourdain, Alessandro Finazzi Agrò, Lionel Breton, Mauro Maccarrone (2012) Endocannabinoids stimulate human melanogenesis via type-1 cannabinoid receptor. J Biol Chem 2012 May 4;287(19):15466-78. doi: 10.1074/jbc.M111.314880. Epub 2012 Mar 19.

121. K C Berridge , T E Robinson (1998) What is the role of dopamine in reward: hedonic impact, reward learning, or incentive salience? 1998 Dec;28(3):309-69. doi: 10.1016/s0165-0173(98)00019-8.

122. L H Brauer, H De Wit (1997) High dose pimozide does not block amphetamine-induced euphoria in normal volunteers. Pharmacology, Biochemistry, and Behavior, 01 Feb 1997, 56(2):265-272 DOI: 10.1016/s0091-3057(96)00240-7

123. https://www.medicinenet.com/how_many_states_legalized_medical_marijuana_2021/article.htm

124. https://www.aclu.org/report/report-war-marijuana-black-and-white

125. https://www.cnbc.com/2021/07/01/in-billion-dollar-cannabis-market-racial-inequity-persists-despite-legalization.html

126. Bernard R. Ortiz de Montellano, (1993) Melanin, Afrocentricity, and Pseudoscience. Yearbook of Physical Anthropology 36:33-58. 1993

ANSWERS

MELANIN QUIZ 1 – WHAT IS MELANIN?

1. - D   **4.** - C
2. - D   **5.** - C
3. - B   **6.** - D

MELANIN QUIZ 2 – DIFFERENT TYPES OF MELANIN

1. - C   **5.** - A
2. - D   **6.** - D
3. - A   **7.** - B
4. - D   **8.** - A

MELANIN QUIZ 3 – EMBRYOGENESIS

1. - C   **5.** - D
2. - B   **6.** - A
3. - D   **7.** - A
4. - D

MELANIN QUIZ 4 – THE IMPORTANCE OF PIGMENTS

1. - A   **5.** - B   **9.** - B
2. - B   **6.** - A   **10.** - C
3. - B   **7.** - C
4. - D   **8.** - D
5. - B

MELANIN QUIZ 5 – MELANOGENESIS

1. - C   **5.** - D   **9.** - D
2. - B   **6.** - B   **10.** - B
3. - D   **7.** - D
4. - B   **8.** - A

MELANIN QUIZ 6 – FOODS FOR MELANIN

1. - D   **5.** - C   **9.** - D
2. - B   **6.** - B   **10.** - A
3. - D   **7.** - B   **11.** - C
4. - A   **8.** - A   **12.** - B

MELANIN QUIZ 7 – WATER FOR MELANIN?

1. - D	**5.** - C
2. - A	**6.** - B
3. - D	**7.** - D
4. - B	**8.** - A

MELANIN QUIZ 8 – MELANIN CONFUSION

1. - D	**6.** - A
2. - B	**7.** - B
3. - B	**8.** - A
4. - C	**9.** - C
5. - D	**10.** - A

MELANIN QUIZ 9 – MELANIN DECODED

1. - A	**5.** - C
2. - C	**6.** - A
3. - D	**7.** - D
4. - D	

MELANIN QUIZ 10 – CODE OF SILENCE

1. - A	**6.** - B
2. - B	**7.** - A
3. - C	**8.** - D
4. - D	**9.** - D
5. - A	**10.** - B

MELANIN QUIZ 11 – MELANIN & MARIJUANA

1. - D	**6.** - D
2. - C	**7.** - A
3. - D	**8.** - B
4. - B	**9.** - D
5. - A	**10.** - D

MARSHALL'S MELANIN TIPS

Melanin is like a battery that continuously needs to be charged up. So here are my top tips for charging up your melanin. I created these tips for you to use as a reference point, because I always get asked questions like, "How do I strengthen my melanin?" or "How do I increase my melanin?" In order to increase your melanin, you need to increase your P.O.W.E.R.S.

P.O.W.E.R.S is an acronym that I made up based on the science I have learnt about melanin over the years. This book covers that science, so the P.O.W.E.R.S acronym should make total sense to you, since you now know the true science of melanin. Be sure to read the book over and over again to really absorb the knowledge. You should be trying to increase your P.O.W.E.R.S daily! So, what does P.O.W.E.R.S stand for?

P is for Plants

Increase the amount of plant foods you consume to ensure you're getting all the right nutrients for melanin. Including aromatic amino acids, antioxidants, vitamins and minerals. Eat the full spectrum of colours (ROY-G-BIV) for optimal health. A good rule of thumb is to "eat the rainbow" throughout the day; starting with red, orange and/or yellow (ROY) pigmented foods in the morning, preferably in a juice form. Watermelon, grapefruits or lemon water are all good examples of what could be consumed first thing in the morning. Then consume more greens (G) throughout the day before finishing with darker coloured fruits and vegetables (BIV). This will ensure your melanin assimilates all the different types of pigments provided by Mother Nature, leading to an increase in melanin function.

O is for Oxygen and Omegas

Increase the amount of oxygen within the body by exercising, meditating (conscious breathing) and being around lots of greenery (like a park). Remember plants breathe out oxygen and we breathe it in. Oxygen is needed for every cell in our body to live and breathe.

Increase the amount of omega-type fatty acids (especially omega-3) in your diet. Omega 3 is anti-inflammatory, so will aid in pain reduction and inflammation. Plus remember, both omega-3 and omega-6 are precursors to your endocannabinoids; and endocannabinoids aid in reducing pain and enhancing feelings of pleasure.

W is for Water

Hydration is key to your melanin health. Drink more structured water from juicing dark green leafy vegetables; and ensure that your body is structuring internal water by basking in the sun, walking bare feet on the earth and exercising. Melanin splits the water molecule into hydrogen and oxygen and can reform it too. This acts as an on/off switch for human electricity which powers our cells.

E is for Exercise and Earthing

Exercise is a great way to increase the flow of electrons (electricity) inside the body. This electricity is what powers all your biochemical processes and keeps your organs charged up. Additionally, exercising creates internal heat (infrared radiation) which helps to structure water internally.

Earthing (or grounding) connects people to the Earth's natural healing energy. It is one of the most overlooked factors in health, yet one of the simplest. Earthing reduces inflammation, pain and stress, improves blood flow, sleep, and vitality. Plus, it's great for infrared radiation. The Earth emits infrared and free electrons which your feet absorb. Earthing in sand is best! Take advantage of the free electrons that the Earth emits by grounding your feet on a beach whilst soaking up the sun.

R is for Rest and Rhythm

Melatonin aids in the repair of DNA cells at night, which makes rest (sleep) an integral part of melanin health. Melatonin regulates melanogenesis, so your circadian rhythm (internal biological clock) needs to be ticking on time. How would you know if your circadian rhythm is 'on time'?

- Deep REM sleep (lucid dreams)
- Waking up around the same time every morning without an alarm
- Waking up feeling refreshed and recharged
- Having a bowel movement in the morning
- Waking up with high testosterone levels. Guys, this means "morning wood." When you were younger this was a common thing. It should still be common as you get older or your circadian rhythm and melanin production may be out of sync.

195

If you're struggling to sleep or you're just not getting quality sleep, consider these things:

Create a bedtime routine
- No eating heavy after 7pm
- Switch off all electronics after 8pm
- Read before going to bed or...
- Meditate before going to bed or...
- Listen to soothing music in bed
- Sleep in total darkness (use blackout bedroom curtains)

Additionally, the R in P.O.W.E.R.S. stands for RHYTHM. And not just circadian rhythm, but rhythm in general. Melanin makes us a rhythmical people. So, we should be listening to music daily, doing a rhythmical movement routine daily (like stretching or yoga or just dancing) and doing some conscious breathing rituals daily. Every living organism has a natural rhythm to it. Align yourself with your natural rhythm by doing things you love on a routinely basis. This will help to activate your endocannabinoid system as well.

S stands for Sunlight

Melanin's number one nutrient is sunlight. It needs UVA to activate nitric oxide in the skin, UVB to synthesise Vitamin D and Infrared radiation to structure water. Remember, sunlight through the eye in the morning is what initiates melanogenesis, so morning sun gazing is highly recommended. If you are indoors all the time, your melanin will be weak. If you are outdoors but never expose your skin or eyes to the sun, your melanin will be weak. Any chemicals that you put on your skin to block the sun will weaken your melanin. Anything that disconnects you from touching the Earth (whether it be your hands touching trees and plants, or your feet touching soil and sand) will weaken your melanin. Allow the sun to be your wireless charger and the Earth to be your plug: HUMAN ENERGY POWERED BY NATURE

Be empowered by the things you've learnt in this book and allow it to guide you to a better knowledge of self and science of self. I truly hope this book serves you well.

One love
Leon Marshall

Figure 53
Human Energy Powered by Nature

DAILY YOU MUST INCREASE YOUR
P.O.W.E.R.S.

Plants
For your electrolytes, vitamins, minerals, anti-oxidants, plant pigments

Oxygen/ Omega's
For your cellular respiration and essential fatty acids

Water
Hydration is key to melanin health. Drink structured water

Exercise
Movement, Electron flow. Health = Energy = Movement

Rest
Repair, Replenish, Rejuvenate, Rhythm

Sunlight
For melanin (in particular UV B sun rays)

Figure 54
P.O.W.E.R.S. poster

2-AG 160, 166, 171–172

A

Acid 25, 29, 31–32, 38, 65, 77–78, 82–85, 87–88, 90–91, 93, 96, 102–104, 117, 121, 134, 163, 165, 194

aerobic 53, 140

Afrocentricity 175

aging 82, 93, 106, 133

Albert Einstein 13, 124, 128, 137, 176

alchemy 178

alkaline 29, 96, 100–104, 108–109

amino acid 31–32, 38, 65, 77–78, 82, 84–85, 87, 90–91, 93, 96, 102, 121, 194

anandamide 160–161, 163–166, 168–169, 171–172

Ancient Egypt 4, 178

animals 19, 29, 53, 68, 85, 97, 119, 168

anthocyanin 51, 62, 81–82, 89, 135

antioxidant 23, 51–52, 60–62, 66, 81–82, 89, 93, 132–135, 142, 194

aromatic 23, 77, 85, 87, 90–91, 93, 121, 194

atom 14, 85, 96–97, 99, 102, 118, 120–121, 123, 134, 137–138

atomic 14, 120, 150, 152

auditory 24, 51, 55, 158

B

Beta-Carotene 91

biochemical 18, 26, 44, 96, 119, 141, 160, 169, 171, 195

Biochemistry 20, 54, 120, 150, 177, 206

bioelectronics 4, 153

biology 4, 49, 52–54, 62, 66, 113, 118–119, 152–153, 178

black hair 31

Black Light 127, 130

Blacks 148, 158

blood 5, 19, 36, 47, 49, 53–54, 66, 74–76, 79, 83, 92, 114, 116, 119, 137, 145, 148–149, 154, 158, 195

blue light 50, 71–72, 75, 79

bone 43–44, 47, 51, 145, 148

bones 32, 38, 49, 87, 116, 133, 137, 145, 148, 150, 154, 159

brain 12, 18–19, 23, 26, 28, 31–36, 38–39, 41, 44, 49–52, 66, 73–74, 82–83, 96, 107, 114, 133, 136, 146, 150, 158–161, 167, 169, 176, 179

breast milk 166–167, 170

C

calcium 116, 145–146, 148, 150

cancer 5, 52, 76–78, 82–83, 92, 144, 151–152, 155

cannabinoids 160, 162, 164–165

cannabis 160–165, 167, 169–171

carbohydrates 120–121

carbon 10, 14, 21, 25–26, 63, 85, 119–121, 123, 130, 178

carbon dioxide 21, 25–26

carcinogenic 149

Carotenoid 51, 62, 91

CBD 161–163, 165, 169, 171

CBDA 165

CBG 171

CBGA 165

cellular pigments 53, 63

central nervous system 23, 146, 160, 175

chemical 10, 14, 18–22, 25–26, 31–32, 38, 49, 52, 54, 62, 65, 67, 75–76, 82, 88–89, 97, 109, 114, 118–120, 123, 130, 132, 136, 138, 157–159, 161, 164–165, 168, 171, 196

chemistry 4, 29, 36, 49, 53–54, 88, 119–120, 134, 153, 168, 178, 181

chlorophyll 18, 20–22, 25, 38, 51–52, 54, 62–63, 100–101, 114, 116, 118, 129, 132, 136, 139, 141, 144

circadian rhythm 49–50, 66–69, 71, 73–74, 168, 195–196

citric acid 102

cocaine 20, 72, 157

colour 4, 10, 18, 26, 29, 31, 33, 36, 49, 51–55, 57–58, 60–61, 63, 65, 72, 81, 87, 93, 119, 127, 138

common sense 12–13, 60, 104, 125, 142, 148, 177

computer 50, 53, 72, 136, 140, 177

copper 31–32, 63, 87–90

coronavirus 73, 145

Cosmic 19, 121, 124, 130

COVID-19 76, 152, 155, 165

cytochrome 52–53, 63

D

dance 116, 170

Darkly Pigmented 33

diabetes 52, 75–76, 92, 162

digestive system 43, 47, 52, 90, 115, 137, 146, 161

Digital Health Care 153

DNA 12, 18, 23, 25–26, 54, 69, 73, 102, 106, 113–115, 118, 123, 129, 144, 149, 155, 195

DOPA 31, 65

DOPAquinone 31–32, 65

Dr. EnQi 10, 136

Dr. Sebi 10, 84, 96, 119–121, 123, 163

drugs 19–20, 31, 35, 72, 76, 145–146, 157, 171

E

ectoderm 43–44, 47, 150

Egypt 178

Egyptian 4, 36, 178

electrolysis 96, 101, 104, 107–109

electromagnetic energy 24

electromagnetic radiation 18, 22, 114, 132, 140, 144

electromagnetic spectrum 55–57, 127, 142

Electromagnetism 178

electron 14, 52, 65, 99, 102–104, 107, 120, 133–135, 138–139, 142, 150, 195

elements 14, 24, 119–121, 178

embryo 41, 43, 47, 49

EMBRYOGENESIS 41, 44, 47, 49, 115, 138, 144, 150, 178

endocannabinoid system 160, 166, 168, 171–172, 179, 196

endocannabinoids 160, 163–172, 194

endoderm 43, 47, 150

enzyme 31–32, 52, 65, 74, 78, 81, 87, 90, 134, 168

epinephrine 54

Estrogen 78, 89, 101

eumelanin 18–19, 28–32, 38, 61, 63, 65, 69, 71, 74, 76, 81–82, 88–90, 92, 94, 100, 119, 132, 135, 137–138, 140–141, 149–150, 153, 155, 157–158, 169

exercise 103, 165–166, 168, 195

eyesight 71, 73

F

fats 60, 83, 102, 123, 163

fatty acid 83–84, 93, 102, 163, 194

fertility 66, 79, 146, 149–150, 154

Fertilization 42, 151

200

Flavonoids 51–52, 135

Food 21–22, 33, 35, 51–52, 60–62, 76–77, 81–84, 90–93, 102, 115, 118, 121, 132, 135, 137, 146, 163–165, 194

Frances Cress Welsing 11–12, 175

free radicals 18, 23, 52, 69, 118, 133–135, 142, 149

fruits 4, 13, 49, 51–52, 60–61, 81–82, 87–89, 91, 93, 97, 102, 105, 115, 121, 134–135, 137, 194

full spectrum 72, 81, 93, 194

G

gastrula 42–43

gastrulation 41, 43–44, 47, 150

genetically modified 88

George Washington Carver 175

glucose 21, 25, 74, 118, 136

GMO 88

H

hair 4, 18, 26, 29, 31–32, 38, 43–44, 47, 49, 65, 74–75, 81, 83, 87, 123, 135, 170

hand sanitizer 76

hearing 19, 33, 41, 51, 114

HeLa cells 151–152, 178

Heme Pigments 52–53, 63

hemoglobin 53

Henrietta Lacks 151–152, 155

hexagon 85, 93, 104, 121

hexagonal 85, 93, 97–99, 104–105, 110, 121

hexagonal shape 105, 121

hormone 50, 66–67, 69, 72, 78, 83, 146, 148–149, 154, 166, 168

hormones 29, 50, 66–67, 69, 72, 78–79, 83, 101, 146, 148–149, 154, 166, 168

Hydrogen 14, 22, 26, 29, 81, 96–97, 99, 101–102, 107, 114, 119–121, 125, 129–130, 132,

138–140, 142, 144, 149, 195

hydroquinone 87

I

immune system 26, 82

intuition 104, 137

intuitive 12, 178

J

jargon 5, 24, 53, 92, 112, 142, 178

jumping 116, 133, 148, 150

K

Kemet 19, 110, 178

Kojic Acid 87–88

L

laptops 50, 71–73, 75, 79, 136

light absorption 12

linea alba 44, 47

linea nigra 44, 47

Locus Coerleus 37

love 10–11, 166, 168, 170, 172, 179, 196

M

marijuana 20, 157–161, 163–164, 169–171, 192

MC1R 29, 31–32

medication 75, 153

melanin batteries 153

melanin centers 12, 150

melanists 175–176

melanocortin 29, 31–32, 50

melanocyte 29, 31–33, 38, 41, 44, 47, 50–51, 65–69, 73–75, 77, 83–84, 87, 96, 137–138, 149, 161, 168

Melanocyte Stimulating Hormones 29, 50, 67

melanogenesis 31, 50, 64–67, 69–71, 73–79, 81–82, 87, 90–91,

201

168, 191, 195–196

melanogenic 52, 71, 74–75

melanoma 52, 118, 149

Melanopsin 49–50, 62

melanosomes 29, 31–32, 38, 65–67, 69, 75, 78

melanotropin 50

melasma 87, 138

Melatonin 50, 66–69, 71–73, 75, 78–79, 90–91, 121, 130, 157, 168, 195

mesoderm 43, 47, 150

Michael Jordan 116

Minister EnQi 10

molecular structure 32, 65, 78, 86, 106, 121–122, 157, 159

molecule 18–20, 22–24, 26, 38, 41, 52–54, 81, 84, 96, 101, 104, 107, 109, 114, 118, 120–121, 129, 132, 138–142, 144–145, 161, 168, 171, 174, 195

motor functions 150

MSH 29, 31–32, 50, 67, 73, 75, 168

music 23, 26, 106, 110, 114, 132–133, 136, 170, 179, 196

N

NASA 123–125, 130, 150–151, 155

nerves 18, 114, 159, 166

nervous system 19, 23–24, 28, 43–44, 47, 49, 52, 66, 83–84, 146, 159–160, 175

Neurology 20, 35, 51, 177

Neuromelanin 19, 23, 26, 28, 33–35, 38–39, 41, 44, 74, 144, 155, 174–175

neurons 24, 35–36, 44, 83–84, 120, 150

neutrons 14, 120

nitric oxide 92, 116, 145, 149, 154, 196

O

Omega 3 90, 172, 194

Omega 6 83, 172

organic 52, 88, 145

organization 24

organizing 24, 26

oxidation 23, 49, 52–53, 82–83, 92, 103–104, 107, 116, 133–135, 142, 145, 149, 154, 196

Oxygen 14, 21–22, 25–26, 52–54, 63, 69, 81, 96–97, 99, 101, 107, 114, 119–121, 129–130, 132–134, 138–140, 142, 144, 194–195

P

Parkinson's disease 151, 155, 176

penis 31, 137, 145

periodic table 14, 120–121, 134, 178

pH 29, 31, 38, 65, 78, 101–102, 104, 109

pheomelanin 18–19, 28–32, 38, 60–61, 65, 69, 74, 78, 81, 91, 94, 135, 138, 144, 149, 155, 157

phonon 23–24

photon 18, 23–24, 85, 121, 132

Photopigments 49, 62

Photosynthesis 20–22, 25, 52, 81, 105, 118, 136, 138–139, 141

Physics 134, 136, 178

phytocannabinoid 162–165, 167, 171

pigments 4, 18, 21–23, 25, 28–29, 31, 33–36, 48–49, 51–55, 57, 60–63, 65–66, 69, 81–82, 87, 118–119, 132, 138–139, 157–158, 174–175, 191, 194

pineal gland 10, 12, 19, 50, 66–67, 69, 75, 78

pituitary gland 67, 69, 73, 75

plant cell 54, 100

polymer 23, 120, 174

polyphenols 52, 81

pregnancy 5, 41, 44–45, 47, 55, 138, 166

pregnant 44

prism 57

proton 14, 104, 120, 150

Pseudoscience 104, 110, 130, 173–175

PUFA 83, 163

R

radiation 18, 22, 69, 72, 76–77, 79, 92, 100, 103, 109, 113–116, 118, 124–125, 127, 129, 132, 135, 137, 140, 144–145, 149–152, 154–155, 176, 195–196

reduction 23, 31, 107, 162, 166, 194

reproduction 41, 43, 47, 66, 79, 115, 146, 149, 154, 166

respiratory pigments 52–53, 63

respiratory system 43, 47

resveratrol 81–82, 89, 93

retina 50, 72

retinal 49, 66

retinoid 91

Rhodopsin 49–51, 62

rhythm 49–50, 66–69, 71, 73–74, 136, 168, 179, 195–196

Richard King 11, 19, 26, 33, 35–36, 39, 114, 123, 136, 175

running 88, 102, 116, 133, 148, 150, 166, 170, 172

S

SARS-CoV-2 152, 165

sea moss 83–84, 90

Selenium 82–83, 90, 93, 135

senses 12–13, 35, 41, 44, 50–51, 55, 60, 66, 102, 104, 115, 125, 135, 142, 144, 148, 159, 161, 166, 172, 174, 176–177, 194

Serotonin 50, 66–67, 69, 75, 78, 85, 90–91

sex 35, 41, 166–167

skin 4, 10, 18–20, 23, 26, 28–29, 31–33, 38, 41, 43–44, 47, 49–52,
60–63, 65–66, 69, 74–79, 81–83, 87, 92–94, 100, 103, 113–116, 119, 123, 133, 135–137, 142, 144–146, 149–150, 154, 158, 175, 179, 196

sleep 14, 49–50, 66, 69, 71–75, 168, 195–196

Smartphones 50, 60, 71–73, 75, 79, 102, 127, 134, 136

Smell 39, 44, 51, 62, 114

Snowflake Pattern 106

social media 10, 73

sound 12, 19, 23–24, 26, 28, 33, 50–51, 62, 100, 114–115, 132, 136–137, 140, 151, 153, 168, 179

space radiation 151, 155

Space Travel 135, 150–151

sports 11, 51, 116, 148, 150, 170

States of Matter 99

structured water 96–98, 100–101, 103–110, 121, 195

substantia nigra 24, 34–36, 39, 150, 168, 179

sugar 47, 62, 74–75, 77, 79, 105, 115, 123

sulphur 31, 65, 91, 93

sunscreen 69, 76–77, 79, 94, 118, 129

supplementation 92, 148, 161, 165

supplements 72, 94, 148, 164–165

T

THC 157–159, 161–165, 167, 169, 171

Tryptophan 78, 85–86, 90–91, 94

tyrosinase 31–32, 52, 65, 74, 78, 87–89, 168

tyrosinase inhibitors 87–89

tyrosine 31–32, 38, 65, 78, 82, 85–87, 89–90, 93–94, 157

U

ultrafast internal conversion 118, 129, 132, 149

203

ultraviolet radiation 69, 79, 92, 115–116, 127, 144, 149

universal self 178

universe 11–13, 35, 50, 55, 57, 62, 68, 97, 106, 108, 113, 116, 118, 120–121, 123–125, 127–129, 135, 140, 144–146, 153, 162, 174, 176–179

Usain Bolt 43, 116

UVA 69, 116, 144–145, 149, 154, 196

UVB 61, 69, 116, 144–146, 149–150, 154, 196

V

vagina 137, 166

vaginal epithelium 31

Vegan 88–89, 172

virus 145, 165

vision 33, 49

Vitamin A 60, 81, 91–92, 94, 146

vitamin D 12, 61, 92, 94, 116, 145–146, 148–150, 154, 165, 196

vitamin D supplementation 92, 148, 165

vitamins 11–12, 60–61, 81, 88–89, 91–92, 94, 105, 116, 135, 145–146, 148–150, 154, 163, 165, 194, 196

W

Water 19–22, 25, 29, 38, 63, 81, 88–89, 95–110, 114, 116, 118, 121, 129, 132–133, 138–142, 144, 192, 194–196

Water dissociation 98, 139

Water Electrolysis 101

white light 57, 127, 130

X

X-rays 132, 135, 150

ABOUT THE AUTHOR

Leon Marshall is a University Lecturer and the co-founder of **The Hidden Science Academy**. He has expertise in Holistic Health, Fitness, Nutrition and Biochemistry. His sold-out Hidden Science Events have struck a chord with the community due to the way he breaks down Science, Knowledge of Self & Health with simplicity.

Website: thehiddenscienceacademy.com
Email: melaninscientist@gmail.com

BV - #0032 - 200422 - C49 - 229/152/9 - PB - 9781739698003 - Gloss Lamination